D1591569

Guy Harvey
Portraits
From The Deep

Guy Harvey

Portraits From The Deep

WORLD
PUBLICATIONS

Published by
World Publications
460 N. Orlando Ave., Suite 200
Winter Park, FL 32789
www.worldpub.net

Printed in the United States of America

10 9 8 7 6 5 4 3 2 1

Edited by David Ritchie
Design by Tom McGlinchy
All photos by Guy Harvey unless otherwise credited

ISBN 0-944406-54-8 regular edition
ISBN 0-944406-55-6 limited edition

Library of Congress Cataloging-in-Publication Data
Harvey, Guy, 1955-
Portraits from the deep / Guy Harvey.
p. cm.
ISBN 0-944406-54-8 (hardcover : alk. paper) — ISBN 0-944406-55-6
(limited ed. : alk. paper)
1. Billfishes. 2. Billfishes—Pictorial works. I. Title.
QL638.I88 H27 2002
597'.78—dc21
2001007637

"To fish at all, even at a humble level, you must notice things: the movement of the water and its patterns, the rocks, the seaweed, the quiver of tiny scattering fish that betrays a big predator under them. Time ... taught me to concentrate on the visual, for fishing is intensely visual, even — perhaps especially — when nothing is happening. It is easy to look, but learning to see is a more gradual process, and it sneaks up on you, unconsciously, by stealth. The sign that it is happening is the fact that you are not bored by the absence of the spectacular."

— *Robert Hughes*
A Jerk on One End:
Reflections of a Mediocre Fisherman

My life and work is dedicated to Gillian, Jessica and Alexander,
who have tolerated my infatuation with the sea and its creatures,
and have withstood the ordeals of long periods of separation.

ACKNOWLEDGEMENTS

Many people have helped me in my scientific and artistic careers, but without the early influence of my parents, Philip and Josephine, I may never have taken a path which has been so inextricably linked with nature, particularly the ocean. There is no doubt that the beauty and abundance of tropical marine life in my native Jamaica played an important role in my formative years, and my parents' interest in and knowledge of nature rubbed off on me by association.

Since my father passed away in 1983, my stepfather, Professor Eric Cruickshank, has performed admirably and provided a stable second home in Scotland for all of us. Similarly, my stepmother, Ann, herself a keen angler, has always supported my endeavors.

Through the years of school and university in Great Britain, a number of people had tremendous positive impacts on my career as a marine scientist. They are the late Professor Reg Jones, Dr. Bill Cruickshank and Dr. Phil Orkin at Aberdeen University. At the University of the West Indies, Professor Ivan Goodbody, my Ph.D. supervisor, kept me on a straight and narrow path to my eventual goal, while Karl Aiken, Charles Watson and Fred Hanley, my postgraduate contemporaries, provided much assistance. Lesley Wilkins was my best friend, a skillful angler, diver, marine scientist, companion and inspiration at university and through some tough years in Jamaica.

Any period of transition is tricky, none more so for me than when I decided to become a full-time marine wildlife artist. Scotty Boyd, Barbara Currie, Raleigh Werking, Kaye Pearson and Charlie Forman were people who advised, assisted, organized and encouraged my early career as an artist. Mike Leech and the late Elwood Harry, current and past presidents of the International Game Fish Association, provided tremendous assistance. There was no map for this path as a marine artist, but they all helped reduce the trial and error.

Over the years, the Guy Harvey team and its licensees have covered a lot of ground, creating and maintaining a whole new division within the recreational fishing and diving industries. There for me from the very beginning were lawyer and partner Charlie Forman and his wife, Sue Ann, along with personal assistant Missy Grey and Jim O'Bryan at T-Shirts of Florida. My general manager, Steve Stock, grabbed the business side of things by the horns and has done a magnificent job in recent years.

From a professional art perspective, Kent Ullberg and his wife, Veerle, have provided me with all the experience, knowledge, guidance and encouragement that seasoned professionals could possibly pass on to a student. The world's most famous wildlife sculptor, Kent has generously helped me organize and operate a successful art business. He has been with me on expeditions to many of the places described in this book, and we have conducted research and exhibited together often. Perhaps Kent was most valuable in helping me make the transition from fish illustrator to artist.

During the past 15 years, I have fished with some of the great names, but my sincerest thanks go to all the captains and their crews who put me on or in the water with some tremendous fish. Among them: Capt. Bobby DeHart, *Sintra*; Capt. Danny Timmons, *Beastmaster* and *Can't Touch Dis*; Capt. Trevor Cockle, *Hooker*; Capt. Laurie Wright and his wife, Julie, *French Look* and *Balek III*; Capt. Barkey Garnsey, *Chunda*; Capt. Mikey Latham, *Freed 'Em*; Capt. Isauro Urrutia, *Miss England* at Tropic Star Lodge; Capt. Bud Gramer, *Intensity*; Capt. Richard Chellimi, *Gamefisher II*; Capt. O.B. O'Bryan and his wife, Charlene, *Ranger* and *CeeDee*; Capt. Kelley Everett and his wife, Jocelyn, *Northern Lights*.

In the early years in Jamaica, Albert Wright and Bernard Clarke on my father's boat *Pat* got me off to a flying start. In the years following, Dr. Ronnie Duquesnay on *Rags*, Capt. Anthony "Finnigan" Richards on Tony Myers' *Bye-Pass*, Capt. Rueben "Skippy" Bajjo

Jessica Harvey dives with tarpon in Grand Cayman's Tarpon Alley.

on John Marzouca's *Screaming Eagle* and Lloyd on Peter McConnell's *No Problem* all skippered for me on some great blue marlin. John and Jenny Greaves have been the most generous couple ever to grace the island of Jamaica ... and they can fish!

Accompanying me on most of the filming expeditions during the past three years has been my friend photojournalist William "Bill" Boyce. Avid angler, diver, marine biologist, photographer and comedian, Bill has been the perfect team player in our filming of various underwater documentaries. At the other end of these expeditions, Diana Udel of Broadcast Quality Inc., in Miami, has done a first-class job of welding all my footage together. She has produced powerful documentaries that have unique content combined with a strong conservation message.

Supporting me in all these endeavors is a great woman. Gillian, my wife of 13 years, has provided much encouragement, guidance and everyday assistance. She enables me to spend the long hours in my studio, helping with all the administration. She has put up with the weeks of separation while I am on an expedition to some corner of the ocean or on the road in America doing art exhibitions, boat shows and public appearances, and has handled the anxiety of living alone for long periods in Kingston. She is the wonderful mother of my two children. At 11, Jessica is my dive buddy at home in Cayman and increasingly plays a role in the fishing and diving expeditions abroad. Alexander, at 8, can't wait to be 10 so he can become a qualified diver. He, too, is an avid angler who now holds five IGFA junior angler world records; Jessica has 14, of which seven are current.

Finally, I am grateful to David Ritchie at *Marlin* magazine for taking on the publication of this book. Thanks also to the rest of the World Publications staff, especially Tom McGlinchy, Don Hill, Nancy Ogburn, Scott Leon, Andy Hahn and Diana Krummel.

CONTENTS

FOREWORD

By Kent Ullberg, N.A.

Ours is the Blue Planet, and as far as we know the only one like it in the universe. With two-thirds of it covered by water, it's logical that the health of the oceans bears directly on the health of our environment — and, ultimately, human beings. Concern for the environment has become one of the most important political and intellectual issues of our day. Contemporary artists deal with current issues, and it is no coincidence that wildlife art has gained prominence at the same time as the conservation movement.

One of the world's foremost contemporary wildlife artists is my friend Dr. Guy Harvey. He proclaims the importance of the environment in every one of his superb works of art, from massive canvases and murals to the most intimate watercolors and drawings, as well as in his films, photography and lectures. He's a powerful spokesman, and I know of nobody more qualified because he combines scientific knowledge and understanding with an artist's eye.

I've had the privilege of accompanying Guy on many of his underwater expeditions to far-flung corners of the world — from Madeira in the Atlantic to the Great Barrier Reef of Australia, from the Central American coasts to the lonely pinnacle of Cocos Island in the Pacific. These have been some of the most exciting and inspiring experiences in my own career as an artist, and I've learned more about marine life from Guy than from any other man.

Like all the great artists in history, Guy has that singular intensity, the passion to see and experience. To quote the great Swedish wildlife painter Bruno Liljefors (1860-1939) about observing wildlife: "Each series of movements becomes for the viewer a series of revelations of beauty; the quicker the eye, the more beauty he's able to see, and he still comes away with this disconsolate feeling that most escaped him." Guy Harvey indeed has a quick eye. He sees things in his subjects that most of us, even trained observers, miss. And yet he often surfaces from a dive slightly dissatisfied, looking for more.

In his quest for knowledge, he drives himself relentlessly. I can personally attest that Guy Harvey expeditions are no leisure cruises, and not for the faint of heart. The closest analogy in my life has been military boot camp, when I served with the Swedish Seals. This very commitment to understanding, however, is also the key to his success as an artist. Ernest Hemingway often expressed that to write "truly," you need to know your subject intimately. This is still the most powerful advice for an artist in any medium. Interestingly, in the Germanic languages the root word for art (kunst) is "können," which means "knowledge, ability."

Guy has both, and he is a most generous teacher of both. I consider him to be an invaluable source of information about marine wildlife and trust him absolutely as a critic, teacher and sounding board for my work in this field. His fellow artist members of the Society of Animal Artists still comment on the unusually informative lecture Guy delivered at their annual forum in 2000. This professional art society is highly regarded internationally, and its members are elected by peers from around the world.

Guy Harvey has many followers and not a few imitators. Look closely, and you'll often spot his distinct gesture of a marlin in other artists' images. But with this book, it's time to honor Guy for his undeniable leadership in today's marine wildlife art movement.

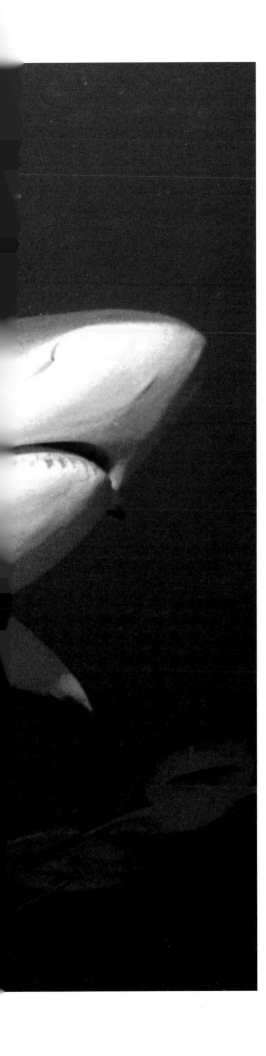

INTRODUCTION

By Charlie Forman

You are about to embark on a literary journey that will take you through the life of Guy Harvey. *Portraits From the Deep* is a rich and wonderful account of the family, the times, politics and forces that have carried Guy from his cattle-country start at the Woodstock farm to the four corners of our planet in search of knowledge and marine adventures.

It also is a story about the unprecedented changes for big-game fishermen and divers that have taken place from the 1960s to the present. Guy has been at the epicenter of this transition. Throughout his life, Guy has found new ways of seeing and appreciating the marine environment. Reading his story allows each of us to gain a better understanding of the earth's majestic waters.

We have just finished an extraordinary half-century of technological transition — from jet airplanes to space shuttles, from slide rules to gigabyte laptop computers. Like everything else in our lives, fishing and diving underwent incredible technological advancements. As I sit here preparing for Club Nautico de San Juan's 48th billfish tournament, I am struck by the fact that I have no idea why Scotty has put the chartreuse "glow in the dark" line on my reels.

Like Guy's, my first fishing line was "semirotten" linen. This was quickly replaced with braided Dacron. About the same time, my Uncle Hamilton was reputed to be the first person to catch a Bahamas bluefin using the "new" monofilament line. Fast-forward about 40 years, and open one of today's major catalogs. You will find more types and qualities of line than I could list in the rest of this introduction.

Unfortunately, most of this technological explosion has just been a process — changing how we do things or the tools we use, but not changing us or the reasons we do the things we do. In many ways, we have not used this technological process to further personal progress. One of the most outstanding exceptions is the enormous headway divers and fishermen have made in how they view, use and conserve their marine environments.

No longer do we rip live coral from the reefs for home decoration. No longer do we kill every billfish to be weighed and photographed back at the dock. Today, reefs are to be seen, photographed and studied, not touched. Today billfish are caught using circle hooks in "release-only" tournaments. Preservation, management and conservation have become the watchwords we live by.

Huge changes that displace thousand-year-old ways of doing things do not come easily. Only through the focused efforts of gifted people who can see things the way they are, imagine things the way they should be, and have the ability to teach the rest of us the difference can true progress be precipitated.

Through his artwork, Guy Harvey has shown us the incredible beauty of the oceans and all the animals that swim in or fly above them. As a teacher, Guy has made us aware of the intricate and fragile balance within which this ecosystem resides. And through his leadership with key organizations and events, he has helped forge the social and political alliances for change that created the public awareness that made progress possible.

From catching fish to studying fish to painting fish to swimming with fish, Guy has done it all. His life is unique and unrepeatable. I would not trade any of the wonderful experiences we have shared, and now you can share them, too. This is one journey you'll be happy to have experienced. Enjoy the book.

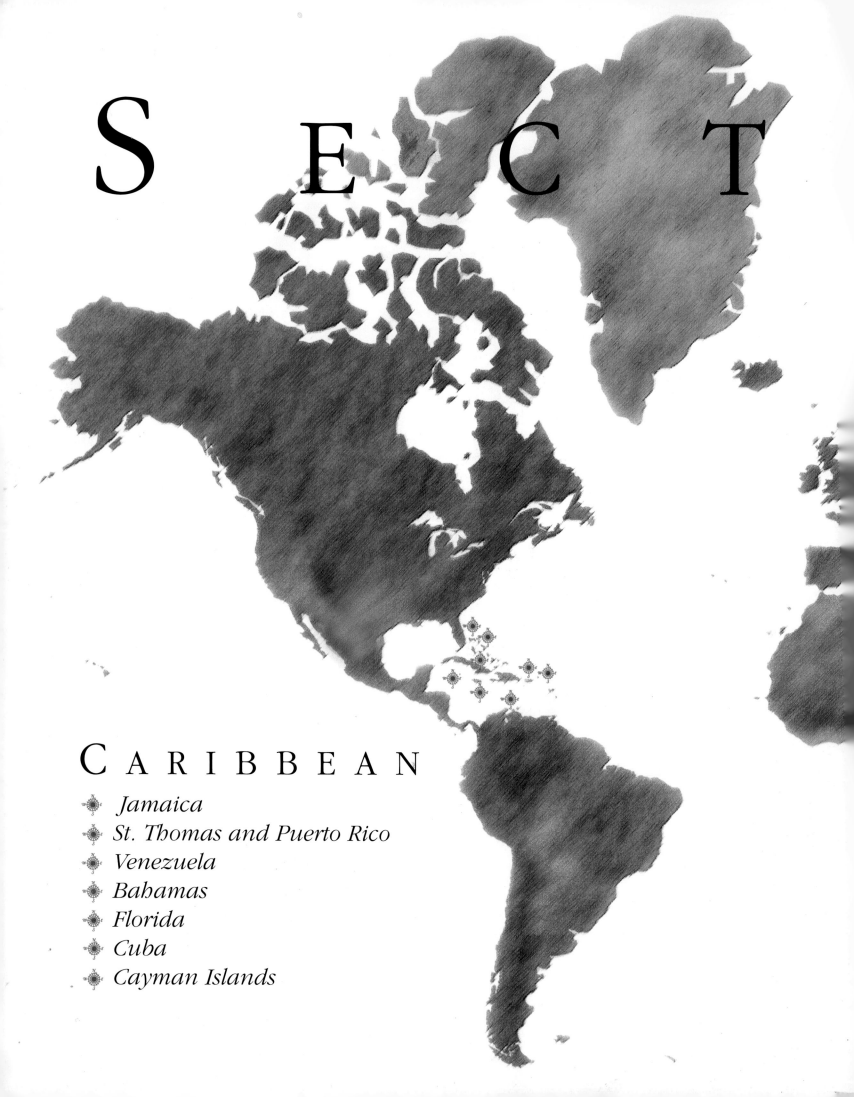

S E C T

CARIBBEAN

- Jamaica
- St. Thomas and Puerto Rico
- Venezuela
- Bahamas
- Florida
- Cuba
- Cayman Islands

CHAPTER 1

JAMAICA
The Early Days

The Amerindian race called the Arawaks set foot in Jamaica in about 1000 A.D. They generally lived a coastal existence, depending on agriculture and fishing for subsistence. Columbus reached Jamaica in 1494, and Spanish colonization began shortly after, with a settlement at Nueva Seville on the north coast. It did not take long for the Spanish to annihilate the Arawaks, who were used as slaves and succumbed to their harsh treatment and diseases. Jamaica had no gold and so was used throughout the 16th century as a provisioning center for more prosperous regions of the Spanish empire. The English captured Jamaica in 1655, and while it remained a base for pirating for most of the 17th century, it had potential for sugar production and soon became an extension of the plantation system already established in the eastern Caribbean.

The Williams family, my mother's ancestors, came to Jamaica in 1664, nine years after the English took over the island from the Spanish. They had received land in return for favors to their cousin, Oliver Cromwell, during the English Civil War, which ended in 1645. Cromwell had devised a strategy for the development of the newly acquired territory called the Western Design. On the old maps "Williams" was written across a large area of southwestern Jamaica now known as the Parish of Westmoreland. From 1730 and for the next century, Jamaica served as one of the world's top sugar-producing nations. The decline began before emancipation in 1838 and continued throughout the 19th century, but other crops such as coffee, pimiento, bananas and citrus featured in Jamaica's exports.

By the time I came along in 1955, land ownership had been reduced to a few cattle properties in the hills 15 miles inland from the south coast. I grew up on one of these, a beautiful property called Woodstock. Having served in the British Army for 14 years, my father, Philip, assumed the running of this property from his father. My mother, Josephine, was raised on the neighboring property of Kew Park. She is a naturalist and dabbled in painting, a talent inherited from both the Harvey and the Williams families.

Both my parents fished a great deal. In the early days, they fished with Zachy Clark, a local fisherman from the small village of Belmont. My father then purchased a 27-foot

Above: A young Guy Harvey catches mountain mullet in Sweet River, Westmoreland, 1961.

Left: Island Blue, *watercolor.*

dugout canoe with an outboard engine for power and bamboo outriggers. The fishing was tremendous, and I recall their stories of the screaming reels tormented by powerful wahoo and tuna. They used linen line, which they meticulously washed, dried and rolled on round wooden drums after each trip — a far cry from today's durable nylon.

They would troll over a number of banks just off this part of the coast, but as children, we were not allowed to go offshore until the age of 8. On the farm we did a fair amount of horseback riding, bird shooting and fishing in the ponds. My sister Philippa became very enthusiastic about horses, which prepared her for a successful career in show jumping and the riding profession. After some close shaves and rough treatment from the horses, I reckoned fishing was a more interesting hobby, and so during school holidays I spent more time fishing with Dad in the canoe.

Dad and Zachy, who always drove the boat, trolled with three lines. Two were rigged with feathers and skipping ballyhoo for smaller fish, and one with a wire line and strip bait for the big fellows. The wire line was a tough one to reel in, so we brothers took turns; my elder brother, Jonathan, was just as keen a fisherman as I was. We caught our share of blackfin, skipjack and bonitos, plus a few wahoo and dolphin. But everyone talked about the blue marlin like it was some kind of god to be worshipped.

Occasionally my parents would charter the *Pat*, a sport-fishing boat captained by Oliver Holroyd-Smyth, an Irishman. The *Pat* was a 32-foot wooden-hulled, custom-built fishing boat with a flybridge and single Chrysler gas engine. It was based out of the Blue Water Fishing Club near Whitehouse on the south coast. Ollie, as my parents called him, though a more appropriate name would have been Captain Bligh, took his charters 12 miles out to a place called Windward Bank. The big, open cockpit was quite an upgrade from the canoe — I could understand why my Dad chartered it frequently. We fished for marlin on the way out to the bank and on the way back. At the bank we caught kingfish and wahoo until we were exhausted. I loved the action — fishing was definitely my thing. Ollie sat hatless up on the bridge all day long in the hot sun with no Bimini top, driving. He frequently bellowed down orders at the mate, Albert Wright, and the anglers. The only time he came down was to reel in a fish when all the other anglers were busy doing the same. Under no circumstances was anyone else allowed up on the bridge.

Dad caught his first blue marlin with Ollie on the *Pat* in May 1957 off Negril, at the western end of Jamaica. On January 7, 1962, my mother caught her first blue, a 203-pounder that at that time set the ladies' record for Jamaica. That same day, fishing on the *Pat* off Lances Bay, Dad caught a marlin of 206 pounds while taking the boat around from Negril to Montego Bay. Later that year, Dad finally caught a small blue in the canoe.

The Port Antonio International Marlin Tournament was inaugurated in 1959. Dad took the canoe around the coast 150 miles to Port Antonio to compete in that tournament, as well as the one in 1960. They had many bites but failed to catch a marlin. In the 1961 event he teamed up with Teddy Lyon-Hall on his Egg Harbor *Joanne* and caught the tournament's first sailfish. Meanwhile, Ollie was chartered for these competitions, and the *Pat* consistently placed over the years, winning in 1964 and 1965.

The Port Antonio tournament grew rapidly in the early 1960s, attracting 178 anglers in 1962. Many overseas teams competed; they came from the U.S., England, Germany, Bermuda, Puerto Rico, the Bahamas, the Dominican Republic and the eastern Caribbean. It was a gentleman's event. Well-known angling personalities such as John Rybovich, Peter Benoit and Doug Bournique attended, and Dr. Don DeSilva from the University of Miami came to collect biological data from the weighed marlin. I remember helping Don cut open the fish to take samples; I was a biologist in the making. I

The Harvey home known as "Woodstock," located in the interior of Jamaica.

Oliver Holroyd-Smith pilots the sport-fishing boat Pat *from its unadorned bridge.*

was proud of my parents for competing annually in the tournament against some of the top names in sport fishing, and the friendships formed in those early years lasted a long time. Port Antonio became my Mecca. Its name was synonymous with marlin, and whenever it was mentioned my heart raced.

In August 1962, Jamaica gained independence from Great Britain. The next year I was shipped off to the Marlborough House boarding school in Kent, England. I was terribly homesick even with Jonathan and other friends from Jamaica there. I found consolation in sketching animals, birds and fish from the Caribbean.

We did a lot of fishing the following summer. One day in July 1964 on our way in from Windward Bank, my mother hooked a blue marlin and fought it for over an hour. It jumped only three times, and I recall my bitter disappointment at seeing its broken bill. Heavy rain fell during the fight and obscured some of the action, but when Ollie and the mate, Albert, pulled the marlin in the boat, I felt privileged to be in the company of such a great fish. The cold rain brought out the vivid blue stripes as I examined every detail. I could not imagine what a thousand-pound marlin must look like. I had read *The Old Man and the Sea* a hundred times, and here in front of me finally was the fish I held in highest esteem.

In August we were fishing with Ollie and Albert on the *Pat* just off Booby Cay, Negril, when I got the chance to see a marlin eat the bait. I was up on the bridge sitting on the cabin roof next to Ollie (there was room only for the driver) when the marlin suddenly appeared behind the right rigger's skipping ballyhoo and ate it. The sea was flat calm, and the marlin put on a tremendous display before being boated. At 145 pounds, it was a typical-sized blue for our corner of the Caribbean. From that day on I set my sights on catching a marlin for myself; I worshipped this magnificent creature! But that was not to happen for many years, as school became the priority. Nonetheless I received detailed accounts of any fishing action in letters from Mum. I fed my craving for fishing with prolific paintings of the fish of my dreams. I was fortunate that the school had a wonderful art teacher, Gillian Cresswell, who encouraged my preoccupation with Caribbean wildlife, particularly the fish.

Swimming, water polo and diving were Harvey's main sports during high school and college.

In 1969 our world flip-flopped when Mum and Dad separated and then divorced. In a little bit of wife swapping, my dad married Ann Cruickshank, and my mother married Ann's first husband, Eric. The Cruickshanks lived in Kingston, and we had known them for many years. Dad and Ann used to go snapper fishing together at night. Apparently Dad was catching more than fish on those excursions. Mum moved to Kingston where Eric was Professor of Medicine and Dean of the Medical Faculty at the University of West Indies. It was a lot for us to handle, but spending so much time away from my family dulled my instinctive rejection of the situation. Peggy Morgan, a close friend of Dad's and Ann's, purchased the *Pat* from Ollie, who was leaving Jamaica, and gave them the boat as a wedding gift! So we continued to fish. Life would be OK.

At that time I began attending a prominent English public school called Sherborne in Dorset. ("Public" really means "private" in England.) I was no great academician, but I enjoyed the rugby, hockey, cricket, swimming and rifle shooting. One term, in the spring of 1971, I wrote my own version of Ernest Hemingway's story for an English class project. It was called "The Young Men and the Sea," and was based on my fishing experiences with the local fishermen from Belmont. The well-illustrated story ends up with three friends catching and bringing home a giant marlin, having successfully fought off the sharks.

I struggled through 11 "O levels," which was an average achievement, then in 1973 did poorly in my "A levels." I barely scraped through in both chemistry and even art classes, and I failed biology and geography. The decision was made — I had to return to a school in Edinburgh to retake biology and geography A levels. It was a low point

*Josephine and Philip Harvey weigh a pair of marlin on
January 7, 1962, with the help of Capt. Oliver Holroyd-Smith
(left) and mate Albert Wright (right). The 203-pound blue was
Josephine's first marlin; Philip's fish weighed 206 pounds.*

Harvey poses with his first blue marlin caught October 4, 1973, accompanied by (left to right) Albert Wright, Pam Williams, Bernard Clark, Denise Williams and father Philip. Pat finished first in that year's Port Antonio tournament thanks to four blue-marlin catches.

in my life, but I learned the valuable lesson that a job worth doing is worth doing well.

When things aggravated me in school I retreated into my fish art. The process of conveying familiar images to paper was reassuring. Painting was always uplifting, and it carried me through this testing period, which essentially had been a step backward. During those long, cold, lonely evenings in Edinburgh, I made steady progress on the series of drawings depicting *The Old Man and the Sea*.

However, the highlight of 1973 was undoubtedly the fishing, thanks primarily to the *Pat* winning both the Montego Bay and the Port Antonio tournaments. In the first event I had to settle for catching a big oceanic white-tip shark which had threatened to eat a marlin that Dad's friend Gordon Langdon, the ex-commissioner of police, was fighting. In Port Antonio, I set my sights on catching my first marlin. We caught nothing during the first two days. Late in the afternoon of Day Three, my cousin Denise caught her first. I was chomping at the bit! Marlin all around, but I had to wait another day. On October 4, 1973, I finally caught my first marlin about a mile outside Ship Rock. It took 40 minutes. In those days we did not back down much on a fish; we fought them to a stand-still from a dead boat. On our way into the marina we got lucky and caught another, a nice marlin of 222 pounds for my Aunt Pam. Mine was 145 pounds, and the two fish moved us into second place. On the last day, I caught a small blue of 77 pounds, which was enough to put us in first place. Trolling back along the north coast after the tournament, I caught another blue off Galina Point. After several years of trying without success, I had caught three blues on three consecutive days. I was thrilled!

After that, I was content to catch just one marlin per year during the holidays before returning to school in the U.K. During one such fishing trip off Negril on my birthday in 1975, we came across a widely dispersed school of sperm whales about 5 miles off the coast. Albert dropped me off to snorkel in the path of the oncoming whales, and I had the encounter of a lifetime. A pair of whales were engaged in courtship. As I approached them, the water grew loud with their noisy chatter. They came to a halt in front of me, as if to look me over. I hung there at the surface, mesmerized. My fascination overcame my fear. If only I had a camera! The male was rubbing the female's head with his, in the same way a horse might rub its neck on a fencepost. After a minute they started swimming again and then, in unison, lifted their tails out of the water above my head and sank below the surface in a graceful swirl. They went straight down, and sounded. The slow undulations of their massive tails propelled them swiftly out of sight into the indigo depths below. All the small fish followed them. I wondered at what point the fish stopped, as there was no way they could follow the whales into the deep, cold, dark world that was the sperm whale's hunting ground. That was the first of several times I have dived with sperm whales off the coast of Jamaica, each one a heart-thumping encounter.

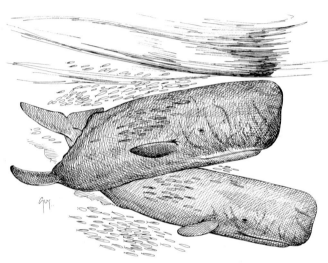

Harvey completed an early black-and-white illustration of courting sperm whales after witnessing such an encounter in Jamaica's waters.

Back to the books. I improved my grades in biology and geography and was admitted to Aberdeen University in October 1974 to complete a Bachelor of Science degree in marine biology. Over the next three years I performed sufficiently well to make it into the honors class for my final year. I served as an integral part of the university's swim and water-polo teams and spent many weekends diving in the North Sea or along the beautiful west coast of Scotland. My Scottish girlfriend, Lesley Wilkins, was also an accomplished diver and a marine biologist completing the same honors course. For my thesis, I undertook an ecological study of the West Indian white mullet in Paradise River, an estuary on Jamaica's south coast. I also collected fish jaws and mouth parts to complete a comparative analysis of feeding adaptations in tropical and temperate fish species. Lesley was working on age and growth studies in the anglerfish and collected her samples from the commercial landings at the vast fish market in Aberdeen. While assisting her at the market I was able to collect all the species I needed and to fend off the lecherous advances crews, who had been at sea for too long, made toward her.

I copiously illustrated both the thesis and the collection with scientific drawings. I found time to help other students with their illustrations, as well as complete the series of 50 drawings based on the Hemingway book. In the summer of 1978, I graduated from Aberdeen with a first-class honors degree. It had all paid off. I accepted a position as a research assistant in the zoology department at Kingston's Mona Campus of the University of the West Indies, and moved back to Jamaica in August 1978.

I started work on my Ph.D. thesis with a fisheries ecology project based at the Port Royal Marine Laboratory, doing research on inshore pelagic species, such as herring, anchovies, jacks and mackerel. Lesley had moved to Jamaica with me and began working on her own Ph.D., studying mangrove oysters, a commercially viable species.

Apart from conducting my own experimental fishing in Kingston Harbour, I befriended some artisanal herring fishermen at the two main fishing beaches to collect better commercial catch statistics and to conduct socioeconomic surveys. A rough crowd populated the Kingston waterfront, a poverty-stricken part of the city, so it took some time to gain their confidence. Political fever ran hot in the late 1970s; the country was in economic disarray and was politically divided. Nowhere was this more apparent than in downtown and western Kingston.

The Jamaica Defense Force Coast Guard headquarters was next door to the marine lab in Port Royal, and during the next year I got to know some of the officers and men very well. My cousin Cmdr. Richard Harvey had founded the Jamaica Sea Squadron, which later became the JDFCG. I joined the Coast Guard Reserves in 1979 as an officer holding a Queen's commission at the rank of sublieutenant. I did this to receive formal training not only in navigation and seamanship, but also in naval diving. And the pay was tax-free. This backfired on me in 1980 when, with an election in the air,

Harvey collects biological data on blue marlin at the Port Antonio Marlin Tournament.

Below: Charles Bryan and Donald Service display their carving of a Harvey-designed tarpon at the Mona Rehab Centre.

politically motivated criminal activity increased dramatically in the country and the murder rate soared. The reserves were called up, and I spent the next two months working street patrols and roadblocks in politically volatile areas. The rival political factions were better armed than the JDF, and we came under fire frequently while trying to maintain peace. More than 800 people were murdered there in 1980.

After Michael Manley and his People's National Party (PNP) came to power in 1972, Manley put Jamaica on a path toward socialism, which resulted in massive nationalization of industry. Productivity plummeted, and his close association with Fidel Castro frightened many people. By 1976, in spite of his poor record, he returned to power. Corruption, now a way of life, infiltrated the electoral system. Middle-class Jamaicans by the thousands left for England, Canada and the U.S. In just a few years, Manley had destroyed a vibrant island economy, increased political tribalism and caused a national "brain drain." The consequential loss of opportunity drove the uneducated working class to desperation. Investment fled the country, and even now, in a new century, Jamaica suffers the consequences of that one man chasing a socialist ideal.

This affected my life and that of my family in many ways. Our farm's productivity fell — no one was buying produce, and what was there was being stolen. Tourists went to other, more friendly Caribbean islands, so Dad's charter fishing operation had few clients. The famous Port Antonio tournament folded in 1977, as middle-class anglers fled the island.

In the 1980 election, the Jamaica Labour Party replaced Manley and his socialist party. Its leader, rightist Edward Seaga, tried to revive Jamaica's stumbling tourism sector and to resuscitate the agricultural and manufacturing potential. Because the people had more faith in Seaga's capitalist policies, the island experienced an upswing in economic activity in the mid-1980s, with a revival in all sectors. Although crime came under control with the increase in employment opportunities, it remained high in Kingston, specifically, and many of us carried firearms for protection. The gun culture of the late

'70s had a firm grip, fueled by simmering political rivalry and widespread trafficking in narcotics.

Tragedy struck early in 1983 when Dad was diagnosed with lung cancer. He had the growth removed, but we did not know at the time that a secondary growth was already far advanced in his brain. He died on my birthday, September 16, 1983, at the age of 59. He had been to me all that a father could be: He had given us a childhood of tremendous fun, along with a rounded education, which he believed was best accomplished in a foreign country. Above all he introduced me to the sea. My regret is that he could not fish with me in some of the places I have visited since his death, places we had discussed many times. Ann sold the family property at Woodstock and then returned to England. It marked the end of an era for me, though it became the beginning of an exciting development in my life.

Graduation day at the
University of West Indies, 1986.

I n 1982 I was struggling to make ends meet as the funding for my research expired. After a short stint working at Morgan's Harbour Hotel and Marina in Port Royal, I realized I could supplement my income by selling my art. I got commissions to do trophies for various fishing tournaments, thereby becoming involved with their administration. I also trained some of the paraplegics at the Mona Rehabilitation Centre in Kingston to carve exquisite marlin trophies out of Jamaica's beautiful mahogany, under the supervision of Jamaica's most famous sculptor, Alvin Marriott. I helped revive the Port Antonio tournament in 1982, and held informal exhibits of artwork in marinas and clubs. These were all successful, especially in Port Antonio, which often had 70 boats registered in the events during the mid '80s — quite a turnaround from the '70s. The fishing was great, and Jamaica received many favorable reports in U.S. fishing journals. In 1986, I was appointed an International Game Fish Association representative for Jamaica. I graduated from the University of West Indies with a Ph.D. and continued teaching at the zoology department.

My new girlfriend and future wife, Gillian Watt, encouraged me to hold two art exhibitions in October 1985, the first at Round Hill near Montego Bay and the second in Kingston. Here I featured the original series of drawings from *The Old Man and the Sea.* With the assistance of well-known artists Beth Hyde, Susan Alexander and Jerry Craig, I reproduced a limited series of 12 prints, with only 100 sets available for purchase. It was my first commercial venture in the world of fine art. Three sponsors believed enough in me and my work to assist in the costs of mounting the exhibition: Tony Myers, Roy DeCambre and Roal Mitchell, all avid fishermen, and people whom I will forever remember as being at the very start of my art career. The exhibitions were successful, and many of the fishing crowd attended.

Overseas anglers, including Scotty Boyd of Boyd's Tackle in Fort Lauderdale and popular photojournalist Barbara Currie, noticed my work early. Barbara encouraged me to donate a set of the "Old Man" series to the annual IGFA banquet and auction in Florida. In addition, Dade Thornton invited me to show my art at a tournament in Chub Cay, Bahamas. Later that year Scotty Boyd arranged a booth for me at the Fort Lauderdale Boat Show. I had no idea my art would do so well in Florida. The show was very successful, and with Scotty's help and connections, it opened up many other opportunities. The most important of these was the beginning of the sportswear licensing program with Raleigh Werking and his company, T-Shirts of Florida in Fort Lauderdale. Charlie Forman, my lawyer and partner and a diving and angling aficionado, expertly handled the legal aspects of contract negotiations and copyright registration.

In January 1987, I suffered a major setback when I had a boating accident in my little Boston Whaler. In my haste one Sunday morning I stupidly started the engine in gear, got thrown out of the boat and ended up in the canal. The outboard propeller mutilated both legs. It cut through the Achilles tendon, cut off the heel and put seven other slices in my left leg. The calf of my right leg was ripped open. My younger brother Piers rushed me to hospital, where an orthopedic surgeon did a great job of splicing the tendon and patching me up. It took a year to recover fully from the injuries.

During my convalescence, I prepared for more shows and tournaments later in the year. Soon I was able to purchase a small house in Kingston and created a studio to increase my productivity. I had been sponging off Piers up until then. The teaching schedule was hectic, and the demand for my art increased. I was soon running out of arms.

One evening, soon after I moved into my new home in January 1988, two gunmen attacked me in my garden. They fired several shots from close range, which just missed. I returned the fire and they ran. When the police finally arrived, we picked up 14 empty cartridge cases. I had been very fortunate, but that close encounter changed my whole attitude toward people. I became hardened and cynical. Life in Jamaica had always been brutal, with the majority of Jamaicans, shackled by their poverty, generally showing indifference to other people, animals and nature. The creeping decline in moral standards, absence of discipline, lack of respect for authority, indifference in the workplace and a corrupt government were symptoms of a population that would soon become ungovernable.

This was most apparent in the aftermath of Hurricane Gilbert, which dealt Jamaica a decisive blow on September 12, 1988. The distribution of relief effort and resources that poured into Jamaica to assist in the recovery was mired in politics. After all the reconstructive work since the debacle of the '70s, the Jamaican voting public indicated a preference for the ailing, sweet-talking Manley, whom the PNP used to regain power in the general election of 1989. Socialism was dead, and there was no real difference in the political ideology of the two opposing parties. When Manley resigned for health reasons in 1991, his deputy, P.J. Patterson, took over. During the next eight years Jamaica underwent an economic decline that made the '70s look like a walk in the park. Successive PNP "victories" in the elections of 1993 and 1997, combined with the corruption of the electoral office, the politicization of the brutal police force and JDF, oppressive taxation and control of the monetary system, and the absence of an effective opposition all pointed to a dictatorship. And yet, so many people relied on the underground economy for survival that it did not matter what the politicians were doing.

By 1995 the annual murder rate had soared to more than 1,000 people per year. I was traveling a great deal in the '90s, and I never felt good leaving Gillian and the two children alone in our house. This form of existence, living behind bars while criminals roamed freely, was becoming ridiculous, and no change loomed. We began to look for safer places to live, now that the disadvantages of living in Jamaica had overtaken the advantages, from my perspective.

We sold our Kingston house and left Jamaica in August 1999 to live in Grand Cayman, the largest of the Cayman Islands. The Westmoreland Parish Council (my home parish) used to administer these small, flat islands, and when Jamaica became independent in 1962, they chose to remain a colony of Great Britain. Today, Grand Cayman is the fifth largest banking center in the world and has a thriving tourism industry based on its natural marine resources. The country promotes all forms of diving and has the highest standard of living in the Caribbean.

Despite the environmental degradation and the deforestation inflicted on some parts of the island, Jamaica remains a very beautiful place. The mountains, rivers, waterfalls, valleys, beaches, tropical foliage and bird life are majestic and unique. The land is rich in natural resources, and anything will grow there. Its people are creative, energetic, athletic, proud, passionate and humorous. Its food and music have penetrated every corner of the world. Where did it all go so terribly wrong?

The author poses with a release flag signifying the first marlin released in a Jamaican tournament. The 1990 Montego Bay Yacht Club event was the country's first partial-release billfish tournament.

Harvey at work in his Kingston studio, 1992.

CHAPTER 2

ST. THOMAS AND PUERTO RICO
Fishing the Tournament Circuit

rior to 1987, my experience fishing for blue marlin was limited to Jamaica and the Cayman Islands, where anglers seldom encounter blues over 200 pounds. For some reason, that part of the western Caribbean just doesn't attract many big female blue marlin. My first exposure to bigger fish came in the USVI Open/ Atlantic Blue Marlin Tournament run by Jimmy Loveland in St. Thomas.

As an observer, I went out on a different boat each day as part of a fleet fishing along the famous North Drop. The action was tremendous: In four days of fishing, 33 boats tagged and released 141 blue marlin, with most estimated in the 250- to 400-pound range. All the boats I observed aboard (*Silky, Beastmaster, Abigail III* and *Bluefin*) had several bites per day; the best day was three blues out of eight bites on board the *Beastmaster*. At one point, in fact, the *Beastmaster* crew was backing down after one marlin while trying to bait another off the bow!

During the tournament's lay day, Jerry Dunaway invited me to ride along aboard his *Hooker*. I stayed on the flying bridge most of the time, watching the action and talking to Capt. Frank "Skip" Smith. They had been hunting records on 8- and 16-pound tackle for several days without success, so Jerry switched over to heavy gear to catch some fish for a change. He soon got into a 250-pound blue and caught it in 20 minutes. The next marlin stayed on the teaser, so his wife, Deborah, pitched a mackerel on a 16-pound rig. During the drop-back, a 400-pound blue came rocketing up from the depths and ate another lure stopped in the water right behind the boat. Instantly the marlin took to the air and jumped across Deborah's line. It did its crazy dance for another half-minute before throwing the hook. I was bug-eyed!

Above: Mate Garry Pemberthy guides the chair as Harvey fights a blue marlin aboard the Sintra. *Photo by Dade Thornton.*

Left: The Strike, acrylic and watercolor, captures a big blue taking a skipping mackerel, a regular occurrence on the North Drop.

Below: The Sintra *crew signed a release flag to commemorate the catch of a blue marlin estimated at 800 pounds.*

*A great day of fishing with Capt. Bobby DeHart
concludes with four blue-marlin releases.
Photo by Dade Thornton.*

Opposite: Blue Tango, *watercolor.*

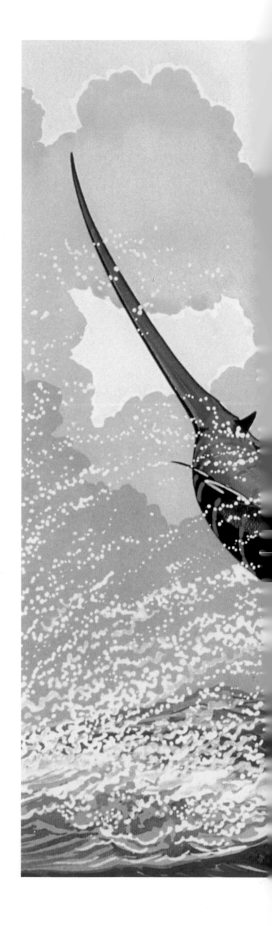

With the unexpected marlin out of the way, Deborah came tight on her fish, and I got my first lesson in light-tackle angling and boat handling. Skip nearly had me off the bridge a couple of times with his rapid changes of direction. After two hours, Deborah had the leader just inches from mate Trevor Cockle's grasp, but the fish proved stubborn and pulled away. On the next attempt the line parted. That's record fishing for you.

I returned to St. Thomas in 1988 to fish aboard John McConnell's *Sintra*, and got another lesson — this time from the fish. We went 0 for 12! Determined to catch a really big marlin, I returned in August 1989 to fish the USVI Open event, again aboard the *Sintra* with Capt. Bobby "Capo" DeHart and mates Garry Pemberthy and Reed Blair. A friend from Jamaica, Mark Wildish, was also aboard as an angler.

We got a late start on the first day and caught zip, which was frustrating because the bite was definitely on. The second day proved much better. Mark caught a 200-pound blue, and I followed in the afternoon with a nice, active blue of 400 pounds hooked just four minutes before lines out at 4:30 p.m. My friend and photographer, the late Dade Thornton, was on board to shoot all the action. We were now on the scoreboard with two fish, but well behind the leading boats, which had at least five.

Day 3 was a great day. Capo put us on four marlin, and we caught and released all four. Mark and I each caught two in the 200- to 300-pound range. The last fish of the day made a memorable show, eating the lure five times before finally staying hooked only eight seconds before lines out. With a day to go we were in fifth place with six blues. The local newspaper, reporting on the event, misspelled Mark's last name as "Wildfish," a moniker that has stuck to this day.

After a lay day on the full moon, we watched as storm squalls pushed through on Day 4. We got only two bites and managed one release on a fine 400-pound blue. We finished in fourth place with seven fish, well behind the winner, *Islamar*, captained by the late Rick Defeo, with 11 blue marlin. The quality of the fishing was tremendous.

We resumed fishing on August 19 and had a quiet day with one small blue, but August 20 was a ripper. It started out with a big blue trying to eat the lure on the long left rigger. As the line came tight, the fish came off and turned away to the right; its tail out of the water looked like a long scythe blade. In the cockpit, watching, we all groaned with disappointment. Capo turned the *Sintra* sharply to port to get back over the fish. As he completed the circle, a huge, black shadow came up and inhaled the short right lure. During the next two hours we never saw the marlin until the mate, Reed Blair, got the leader for the first time. The big blue took off again and fought doggedly for another half-hour before Reed got the leader again and held on. The marlin was on her side, paddling gently as Garry tagged her in the shoulder. Capo shouted at me to jump out of the chair to have a look. The fish was longer than the cockpit, round as a barrel and Capo called her a conservative 800 pounds. We took lots of photos. She started shaking her massive head, the hook came free, then she righted herself and swam off in a flash of neon blue — the perfect release. As the fish was a record for me as well as the *Sintra*, I received a blue-marlin release flag with all the catch information, signed by Capo, Reed, Garry and Mark.

We continued fishing, and Mark released a small blue that was so striped up it looked like a wahoo. Immediately afterward, Mark caught a blue over 300 pounds and then had a bite from a 500-pounder that got away. The bite that day had also been good for the other boats along the North Drop, but it was time to leave. We finished up with 11 blue-marlin releases from 18 bites in six days of fishing — St. Thomas at its best.

John McConnell, the late IGFA President Elwood Harry, Harvey and Mike Hamilton participate in the San Juan International flag ceremony.

T he *Sintra* next moved over to the Club Nautico de San Juan in Puerto Rico, to fish the world-famous International Billfish Tournament in September 1989. In my opinion, this is the best-organized fishing tournament in the Caribbean, and perhaps the world.

Each evening tournament organizers provide marvelous food and entertainment in the magnificent Club House or in Old San Juan, and the Puerto Rican hospitality is unsurpassed. They organize daily guided trips for wives and friends who do not fish, and the tournament committee anticipates every little detail.

The Club Nautico event has benefited from some strong leadership over the years from great personalities such as Estaban Bird, Ralph "Agie" Vicente, Henry Rexach, Roy Camero, Ralph Christiansen Jr., Alberto "Pipo" Gual, Luis Valldejuli and Mickey Tirado. Many other famous fishing characters also fish the event, such as Jaime Fullana, Charlie Donato, Thomas Irizzary and Mike Benitez, to name a few.

Harvey makes a donation to the annual Billfish Foundation auction in San Juan.

Opposite: Jumped Him Off, *watercolor.*

Instead of using observers like many tournaments, this event's rules require each boat to carry three team anglers and to host one rotating angler, who fishes on a different boat each day. Any fish the rotating angler catches count for his team, and the rotation process does a good job of keeping everybody honest. The absence of cash prizes also helps. In choosing a rotating angler and fishing ambassador for our team that year, we decided there could be none better than my good friend, the evergreen Frank Johnson of Mold Craft Lures.

On our first day, the rotating angler assigned to *Sintra* farmed five blue marlin bites out from under us. Very frustrating! On the second day our assigned rotating angler from another team did not show up, nor did the nonfishing observer to replace the missing angler. We left an hour late and an angler short, so we put out three rods (rules require a minimum of three anglers or rods per boat). Garry and I were the anglers, with the third rod manned by a "ghost angler." We agreed that if a fish took that lure

Above: Deja Blue, *watercolor, ranks as Harvey's most*
successful limited-edition print.

Opposite: Blue and Yellow, *mixed media.*

and got hooked, we would automatically disqualify it. At 11:30, I hooked, caught, tagged and released a small blue of 100 pounds. At 1 p.m., as I was watching the lures, I saw a marlin at the surface swimming past the boat. It turned sharply and ate the lure on my rod. Garry shouted out that he had a blue on his rod, and then a third marlin crashed the lure on the unmanned rod. As long as I live, I shall always remember the sight of three blue marlin in the air at once, all greyhounding in the same direction.

I was in the chair, while Garry had the difficult task of standing up to a blue on an 80-pound bent-butt rod, and the third marlin fought itself. When Capo radioed in our triple hookup, he naturally disqualified the third marlin. The radio exploded in a babble of incoherent Spanish as the other captains immediately protested. After 25 minutes, my marlin was brought into the boat as it was well over that year's minimum weight of 200 pounds. Garry then took the chair to finish the fight with his marlin while I began to reel in the third marlin, which by some miracle was still attached to the unattended rod but a long way out. Garry released his fish, and I jumped back in the chair to complete the triple catch, releasing the third blue marlin.

Back in the marina there was a lot of discussion. Our intent was to fish by the rules, as clearly indicated by our own disqualification of the third marlin. The rules simply stated that a minimum of three anglers must fish; the committee had provided neither a third angler nor an observer. However, it did not matter. The fact that we had two anglers manning three rods was viewed as an infraction, and all the fish were disqualified. As the team captain, I apologized to the committee, and we fished the remainder of the tournament. Regardless of the outcome, I will forever consider that day's blue-marlin tripleheader (still the only one I've ever witnessed) a distinct privilege to experience.

We came back the next year to fish the 1990 event and caught one blue and a white, and had a tremendous time socially. A lot of big fish were caught that year. The committee had raised the minimum qualifying weight to 300 pounds, showing an increasing trend toward catch-and-release. By the time I returned to fish the 1994 event with Donna and Jim Robinson aboard the 65-foot Merritt *Can't Touch Dis*, the minimum was at 400 pounds.

Since then I have fished fewer tournaments, and instead began putting more effort into filming free-swimming billfish in the Atlantic and Pacific. The results inspired a number of paintings throughout the years, many of which appear in this book.

CHAPTER 3

*Opposite: The author's first underwater
swordfish encounter: an awesome 300-pound
specimen, just hooked up and swimming at 80
feet. Moments after Harvey took this photo, the
fish turned on him. It remains the only billfish
out of hundreds observed to exhibit aggression
toward a diver.*

VENEZUELA
Grand-Slam Country

I don't remember exactly when I first heard of the La Guaira Bank, but I do know that as long as I've been fishing, I've known of the prolific waters off the coast of Venezuela.

Back in the 1980s, many U.S. sport-fishing boats would head south to Venezuela after the marlin season was over in St. Thomas and stay for the white marlin bite, until Thanksgiving. Many of these boats reported catches of 30 to 50 white marlin a day there, plus plenty of blue marlin and sailfish. It was (and still is) the best place in the Caribbean to catch a grand slam — three billfish species in a single day.

A town called Macuto offered some adequate marinas, with good accommodations and restaurants nearby. The fuel was extremely cheap: A 50-foot boat could fill up for only $45. Local charter operators offered proficient crews and boats, so the marinas were always busy. On weekends the Venezuelans from Caracas would descend on Macuto in large numbers to go fishing and to party.

This was all before the natural disaster in December 1999, when horrendous landslides overwhelmed this part of the coast and thousands of its inhabitants. Recovery has been a slow process, and the sport-fishing community has greatly assisted in that effort, sending food, supplies and money. Although scars remain, most of the area's sport-fishing centers have reopened, and boats are once again plying the waters of the La Guaira Bank.

My first fishing expedition to Venezuela was in November 1988 on the *Sintra*, with Capt. Bobby DeHart and mates Scott Clark and Garry Pemberthy. The *Beastmaster*, with Rus Hensley, his family and crew, was in the slip next to us, so we had a fun time in addition to great fishing. We enjoyed some memorable days chasing those tricky white marlin, and I caught my first on the *Beastmaster* on 20-pound gear. The white is a tough adversary, giving a great account of itself and spending a lot of time in the air. During the week we also caught some big bull dolphin, yellowfin tuna and all available billfish species, including my first spearfish and first broadbill swordfish.

The spearfish looked like a white marlin when it slid up behind the skipping ballyhoo bait on the right rigger. In fact, I didn't realize what it was until Scott had wired it and started shouting, "Spearfish!" and flipped it into the boat. I had never set eyes on a fresh specimen before, and this provided a perfect opportunity for me to study this slim, elegant billfish. It was also part of a grand-slam day.

*Harvey sighted his first free-swimming white marlin
as it chased a teaser behind the* Can't Touch Dis.
*These marlin light up brilliantly in comparison to
sailfish and blue marlin.*

My first broadbill experience will always remain clear in my memory. It was calm on the evening of November 18, so we fished late and then set up for swordfish before dusk, using the usual technique of drifting with two rigged squid and waiting for a bite. Soon after dark I hooked up to my first swordfish on 80-pound gear. I was amazed at the strength of the fish; it took nearly an hour to bring to the boat, where Scott got the leader and Garry did the gaffing. This was my first opportunity in 10 years to look at a swordfish up close, and on the way back into the marina I made notes about its anatomy and coloration. It was a well-proportioned fish at over 200 pounds; its body was short and round like a tuna's, and it had a long bill, a third of its total body length.

The swordfish are so remarkably different from the other billfish, many question why they are grouped in the same suborder, Scombroidei, although they are in a separate family, Xiphiidae. All the other billfish species are grouped in the family Istiophoridae and are related to the tunas and mackerels, the Scombridae.

When painting a swordfish, I have to disregard all my knowledge of billfish anatomy and start over again because of their tremendous differences. The long, flat bill, wide head, huge eyes, small lower jaw and the gill arrangement are all different from those of the Istiophorids. The swordfish has eight branchiostegal bones in the gill flap (seven in other billfish), no pelvic fins, fixed dorsal and anal fins, tiny second dorsal and anal fins, and a single large caudal keel on each side of the peduncle, where all other billfish have two. Swordfish skin has no scales, but has unique longitudinal pleats along its flanks. These major anatomical differences likely evolved out of differences in their ecology. Swordfish typically live in the deeper, colder mesopelagic oceanic zone, while the other billfish prefer the warmer, brighter epipelagic zone near the surface.

I returned to Venezuela in November 1994 with Donna Robinson on her 65-foot Merritt, *Can't Touch Dis.* By then I was seriously into diving with free-swimming billfish, and Donna kindly let me jump in on several whites and sailfish, as well as my first

Moonlight Duet, *mixed media*.

Above: A hooked sailfish, just tagged and about to be released by the crew of the Can't Touch Dis. *The afternoon light proved perfect for close-ups.*

Right: Two sails swim in cruise mode on the La Guaira Bank — sails down and bodies cast in a pastel blue.

Atlantic blue marlin. Capt. Danny Timmons was at the helm, while mates Tony DiGiulian and Antonio teased in enough fish for me to get my first Atlantic billfish images the hard way — while diving with free-swimming fish.

One white marlin was particularly cooperative and spent several minutes around the boat. I shot a whole roll of film on this beautiful creature; I could not get over how striped and colorful the white was compared with the sailfish and blue marlin, which typically displayed black feeding colors. The white did pirouettes around me, chasing the teasers until Antonio could no longer resist and sent out a hooked bait. Hooked up, the white stopped swimming and began to shake its head furiously, gagging and regurgitating partly digested food. Then it raced away to the surface and began jumping all over the place. In seconds it had been transformed from being a swift, marine hunter to a panicked, traumatized fish on the run, but with no escape from the persistent pull of the line. I was horrified, revolted and angry! My naturalist's instinct to admire and respect nature was crushing my hunter's instinct to seek out and catch these elusive creatures.

The hunting instinct is inherent; the naturalist's desire for greater knowledge through observation and study is acquired through education, followed by voluntary exposure. In the end an accomplished hunter or fisherman must also become a naturalist, because he has to learn about an animal's ecology to be successful.

Surely, I thought at the time, there must be a better way to use bait to catch billfish, a way that does not result in their being hooked in the soft throat or stomach tissues. The advent of circle hooks to replace J-hooks at the end of the 1990s was, in my opinion, the greatest single step forward the recreational fishing sector had taken in the conservation of billfish since adopting catch-and-release.

On my most recent expedition to Venezuela, in September 1998, I visited with Bill Boyce and a film crew from the BBC Natural History Unit, including my good friend Andy Byatt and Leo "The Hairy Wart" Dickinson. Leo is famous for his documentaries and his book *Filming the Impossible*. We scheduled 10 days aboard Capt. "O.B." O'Bryan's 53-foot Hatteras *Ranger* to film billfish, tunas and hopefully some bait balls with whales feeding on them.

During our 10 days we dived on numbers of teased-up whites and sailfish; the few blues we raised in the spread were uncooperative. Some of the best experiences were diving with schools of yellowfin tuna feeding on sardines. They would drive the bait to the surface and proceed to consume them in what can best be described as a conveyor-belt feeding system. As I had seen previously with marlins, the tunas do not all feed at once on a bait ball, simply because there is not enough space for all the predators. The tunas feed on the bait ball in a stream of bodies, all going in the same direction, swimming up to the ball, biting and leaving in a smooth flow. Below, the main body of the school is milling, waiting for its turn.

The bait balls were quite small and the tunas consumed them quickly, so Bill and I had to swim to them rapidly after O.B. dropped us into position. As the number of fish in the bait ball dwindled to a few dozen, the bait committed suicide by abandoning the schooling instinct and separating. The tunas made a mad dash to mop up the stragglers, creating a lot of drama at the surface. Bill and I would then dive deep and hang with the vast school of milling tunas, hoping to see a big predator. It was a weird sensation being at 100 feet, surrounded on all sides by beautiful glinting black-and-gold bodies with big staring eyes, yellow fins and tails beating. When they passed, we were left in a blue void, looking toward the surface.

During the week we heard from some of the other charter boats that swordfish were being caught during the day, but down deep. O.B. and I concocted a plan to put a cameraman in the water with a hooked swordfish during the daylight so we could get

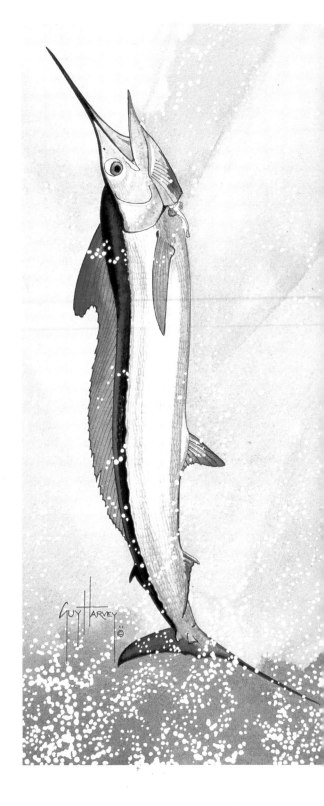

Unnamed longbill spearfish, watercolor. Harvey caught his first spearfish in Venezuela.

Blue Moon, *acrylic on canvas. This large 120- by 50-inch painting was inspired by Harvey's dives with yellowfin tuna feeding on sardines, west of the La Guaira Bank.*

something on film. Swordfish have a well-deserved reputation for being aggressive, and we didn't want to take any unnecessary risks to test this theory. On one afternoon, we tried for a swordfish by drifting two baits close to the bottom in 1,500 feet of water west of the La Guaira Bank.

Fishing for broadbill is a waiting game, so while we waited we swam with passing dolphins and whales. Finally, just after sunset I reeled up a small swordfish of about 20 pounds. At this size, the bill looks disproportionately long, and the fish appears like something out of the Jurassic age. Nonetheless, Bill jumped in and got some still shots of it. The fish was then released in good condition, but not before it gave Bill a nick on the shoulder.

The following day, we started our swordfish efforts earlier in the afternoon. Soon after 4 p.m. I had a bite and began reeling in the large amount of slack line, coming tight on the fish far below. Swordfish hooked in the daytime usually swim straight up

to the surface and then begin their classic, never-give-up fight in the top 200 feet of water. This fish was no different. When the 100-foot marker came up on the reel, I passed the rod over to O.B.'s wife, Charlene, and put on my dive gear. I wanted to verify that it was indeed a swordfish and that we weren't wasting precious daylight on a big shark. I opted to take my Nikonos RS still camera and not the video, a decision I later regretted.

In absolutely crystal-clear water, I saw the fish when it was at 80 feet and swam down to intercept it. I was very excited seeing a swordfish underwater for the first time — it was a good fish of around 300 pounds. It was heading up toward the surface, swimming lazily with the line angled up toward the boat behind me. I swam closer and started taking photographs.

As I approached I began picking out the details. The hook was in the right corner of the jaw; the bill was so long I had to turn the camera and rack the zoom back to 20mm to fit it all in. The fish started to kick harder as I got a final shot looking along its body. Then it pulled away strongly, swam up a few more yards and suddenly turned around and charged straight at me. I was mesmerized — frozen to the spot, totally focused on what was taking place! With great speed the fish approached, but it then stopped abruptly and turned sideways, looking at me with its huge, featureless black eye. I exhaled a blast of bubbles as it turned away and headed up to the surface, where it began jumping.

It was not until I got back to the surface that I appreciated what had just transpired. If that swordfish had wanted to skewer me, it could have done so easily. It was an aggressive move, but I considered it more of a warning, a signal for me not to come any closer. For as long as I live, I will remember that long bill and black fathomless eye giving me the look before the fish turned away.

This was not a very encouraging start to our swordfish campaign.

Back in the *Ranger*, they wanted to know what I had done to the fish to make it so active. I jumped back in the chair and fought the swordfish for another hour and 20 minutes. During this time, we worked on a plan to get the best picture, as the fish would not be happy to see more divers. We would work the fish until it was sufficiently tired that O.B. could lead it in a circle, going back and forth between two divers about 50 yards apart. I would control the tired fish from the chair, using heavy drag on the reel. Notice I did not volunteer to go in again with this fish.

Above: Bill Boyce's first swordfish was a 250-pounder caught aboard the Ranger *with Capt. O.B. O'Bryan.*

LONGLINING IN VENEZUELA

Each evening on the way back to the marina, we had to dodge some of the local longliners in canoes, who set unmarked gill nets and minilonglines day and night for billfish and tuna. Apart from being a hazard, they were depleting the billfish stocks, and one wonders at the destruction of the billfish resource in this location, one of the world's most famous billfishing destinations. One afternoon we were able to film some of the longlining and gill-netting activity, and witnessed both sailfish and white marlin being caught. The local Venezuela charter-boat crews have protested this form of fishing, but they have no legal recourse.

Soon after this expedition, I asked Dr. Ruben Jaen, a friend and IGFA trustee from Venezuela, about the legality of local longline fishing activity. I quote from his response on November 2, 1998:

In 1985, two American hydraulic longliners, the No Problem *and the* Alice Mary, *caught a lot of billfish near La Guaira Bank, and I decided to stop that. Needless to say, they were very angry and tried to bribe the authorities. Finally after a hard lobby, I got a decree from the President of Venezuela to protect the billfish in a zone of 5,000 square miles, with its centre on La Guaira Port. The area is closed for hydraulic longliners and purse-seiners, but not for artisanal fishermen (including hand-line longliners), who have been fishing with nets since 1970. Those people have 27 special permits, and as 70 percent of the Venezuelans live in poverty, they contribute with cheap food for the people of the Federal District. Due to the high cost of the engines and the nets, there are now fewer boats than before. Sport fishing in the area has been very satisfactory during all of the past years, and the blue and white marlin and swordfish are abundant. Of course, I would like to stop the artisanal fishing, but it is almost impossible due to the economic and political situation of Venezuela. But to me, we saved sport fishing with that decree!*

There you have it — life is a compromise.

Charlene got the leader and held on, with the swordfish swimming placidly below. Bill jumped in, camera in hand. The swordfish took off like a rocket, going straight down, allowing Bill only a fleeting glimpse. We dropped off the other two cameramen — Andy and Leo — and for several minutes I tried to pump the "tired" swordfish closer to the surface, to bring it nearer the divers, but it would have nothing to do with them. Finally the 80-pound line snapped.

Despite the premature release, the swordfish bug had bitten deeply, and we continued to try for footage the next day. We didn't get a bite until 5 p.m.; Bill was on the rod, and the swordfish gave him a rough time. Darkness fell, followed by a squall full of rain and claps of thunder. The jagged lightning lit up the sea around us, providing a dramatic backdrop, like being on the front line during an artillery bombardment. After 2 ½ hours, Charlene finally got the leader of Bill's first broadbill, a fish of about 250 pounds.

We concluded our final trip to Venezuela feeling somewhat pessimistic about the possibility of videotaping a free-swimming swordfish during the day. Night would be easier since they do appear around boats drifting for them at night, both in Venezuela and off the Kenyan coast, where fly-fishermen have targeted them with success. Somehow, though, I do not relish the idea of diving at night with swordfish! Perhaps I'll try diving in traps set for tuna in the Mediterranean, where they are sometimes caught, or off the California coast, where harpooning swordfish from "stick boats" remains a viable commercial operation. While the where, when and how still are uncertain, the what remains clear: I must find a way to capture this great fish on film.

A Venezuelan Experience, mixed media. Created for and donated to the 1995 IGFA Auction, this piece was inspired when filming two sailfish and having a blue marlin suddenly join the hunt.

CHAPTER 4

BAHAMAS
The Sharks of Walker's Cay

I n the 1980s and '90s, I went to the Bahamas mainly to fish, often in a blue marlin tournament. My favorite event there was the Bertram/Hatteras Shootout, a three-day invitational event for owners of Hatteras or Bertram sport-fishing boats.

The organizers, Jim Shaefer and Hutch Hutchengs, put on a great show, and a lot of money was up for grabs in the various calcuttas. I first fished the event with John McConnell aboard his two *Sintra* boats — the first a 52-foot Hatteras and the second a 65-foot Hatteras. Both were skippered by the famous Capt. Bobby DeHart, or "Capo" as he was affectionately called. We had a wonderful time, caught some nice fish and even placed second in the 1988 shootout with a fine 592-pound blue marlin. Fellow artist/angler Garry Pemberthy caught that fish, and at the time it ranked as the biggest blue marlin I had seen boated.

Though the Bertram/Hatteras Shootout moved to Boat Harbour Marina at Marsh Harbour, Abaco Island, in the late 1990s, most anglers still equate the event with its long-time home at Walker's Cay, a privately owned island in the northern Bahamas that is self-sufficient with airstrip, air service, generator, water, hotel, marina and dive shop. Like most other Bahamian islands, Walker's Cay offers a tremendous variety of fishing options. Deep water is close by and filled with all sorts of offshore game fish, the surrounding reefs still have abundant grouper and snapper, and the sand flats are home to many permit and bonefish. And don't forget the diving!

Many resort managers have come and gone over the years, but Gary Adkinson has been a fixture in the Walker's Cay program for 17 years, serving in various capacities.

Above: The Big Four, *watercolor:*
Great white, hammerhead, tiger and mako.

Opposite: An up-close portrait of a Caribbean reef shark, the most abundant shark at the Walker's Cay Shark Rodeo.

Above: A mixed school of porkfish and schoolmaster snapper at Shark Canyon, Walker's Cay.

Among the most notable is the "Shark Rodeo" diving attraction he developed along with his wife, Brenda, divemaster Barry Albury and the rest of the dive operations staff. The Bahamas offers many shark dives, but Walker's offers the greatest number of animals, is well-regulated and has an impeccable safety record. In addition, Gary has acquired a reputation as one of the world's most respected authorities on shark behavior. Institutions, dive clubs and film crews come from all over the world to experience what Walker's Cay has to offer.

During my various expeditions to different locations to film billfish, I have encountered sharks with regularity at only two locations — Cocos Island and the Great Barrier Reef in Australia. Billfish and sharks will share space in oceanographic situations like these, where the drop-off meets the deep water, but typically the number of shark encounters diminishes as you move farther out in the tropical open ocean, the domain of the billfish. One reason: Open-ocean sharks seldom co-exist with billfish. They more readily associate with tuna and marine mammals, like pilot whales. Also, in many places overfishing has so depleted oceanic shark species such as silky, dusky, mako and hammerhead that they could be considered rare.

Sharks are fished heavily worldwide because of the increasing demand for their fins, particularly in the Orient. Recently, sharks have received some protection in designated marine parks and through governmental restrictions. Some endangered species, such as the great white, are finally being protected aggressively in countries such as Australia, South Africa and the U.S. Dive operators in these countries now realize the economic benefits of having the animals as a living attraction. Enthusiasts will pay thousands of dollars and travel great distances just for a chance to see these animals in their natural surroundings.

I went to Walker's Cay in June 2000 with a film crew and four scientists from the Guy Harvey Research Institute (see Chapter 5) to accomplish several goals: increase my library of underwater footage of sharks, get close to a variety of species for reference

Above: Incoming Tide, *mixed media. The crystal-clear waters of the Bahamas, crammed with gamefish, provide the perfect opportunity for close encounters with a variety of species.*

Above: Three large bull sharks home in on fish scraps along the northern shore of Walker's Cay.

for my art work, and assist the GHRI scientists in establishing a working relationship with the Walker's Cay dive staff. A major research project on the biology, ecology and population dynamics of the Caribbean reef shark is currently under way at the institute, and the population at Walker's makes up an integral part of the survey.

By using a 100-pound frozen lump of fish heads and carcasses called a "chumsicle," Gary has conditioned the sharks to gather to feed in a specific location in the reef twice per week. Suspended 20 feet off the bottom to prevent sand from obscuring the view for divers and moored to the bottom so the sharks are unable to drag it away, the chumsicle has a steel core to hold the fish bits together. As it melts in the seawater, the sharks begin to feed, taking turns like an orderly procession of diners at a buffet table. Toward the end of the feed, the chumsicle tends to break into smaller pieces that fall away from the steel core, and the process becomes chaotic as sharks race in frantically to grab loose chunks before all is gone. "A tremendous amount of energy is expended in those few seconds, and you don't want to get between the sharks and the food!" says Gary.

During my June visit we often observed as many as 80 individuals of three species of sharks at the chumsicle: the Caribbean reef, the blacktip reef shark and the nurse. The sharks are so used to seeing Gary and Barry that they can work very close to the chumsicle. Gary has already done a lot of tagging and tracking work with his "kids," and many of them carry tags. The sharks also allow Gary to hold on to their tails, bending

them forward and putting the fish into a state of "tonic immobility." He uses this technique to implant tags or to remove hooks prior to release.

Because Gary can work closely with the sharks, the GHRI scientists asked him if it would be possible to take a small piece of tissue from some of the animals for genetic analysis. Using a specially designed tool, Gary targeted passing sharks, obtaining sufficient tissue once in every four attempts. This marked the first time such a technique was used; usually tissue must be taken from caught fish or carcasses. The DNA extracted from these animals helps in identifying the particular species of sharks whose fins and carcasses are filling fish markets around the world. The data will help confirm which species are being most heavily fished. DNA analysis also helps identify any exchange of genetic material in widely dispersed species, such as the Caribbean reef shark. The same procedures would apply to other migratory species, such as tuna and billfish.

Above: The "chumsicle" draws a crush of bodies at the Walker's Cay Shark Rodeo. As long as the chumsicle holds together, the predators feed in a surprisingly orderly fashion.

The chumsicle system of attracting and feeding sharks does not involve hand feeding, which lessens the chance for accidents. It also affords the clients extra peace of mind, freeing them to focus on behavioral observations and photography. I felt very comfortable and relished the opportunity to spend time with these sleek, streamlined, graceful creatures. With so much time to observe so many animals, I could focus on the subtle things such as the remoras, mating bites and the other species of fish swimming with the sharks.

One intriguing thing I observed was the way small bar jacks would adopt a swimming position immediately in front of a reef shark or a blacktip, in a seemingly vulnerable spot. They would ride the pressure wave created by the forward motion of the large animal, matching its every turn with practiced choreography. In reality, these little guys were actually trying to avoid larger individuals of their own species, which would take up position beside the host's dorsal or pectoral fin, waiting for one of the small jacks to lose its place in front of the shark's nose.

This system often broke down at the chumsicle because the sharks halted their forward motion as they fed. The small jacks then found themselves surrounded by a crush of bodies, including a large number of big jacks. The small fish would then flee to the reef for protection, only to be caught out in the open. I witnessed this a number of times at the chumsicle but only twice on the reef. Here the big jacks rushed up one side of the shark, forcing the little guy to dodge away, but straight into the big jacks advancing on the other side. The big jacks had set a trap!

At another site, Gary has been able to bring a variety of sharks — nurse, lemon blacktip, blacknose and the occasional great hammerhead — in close to shore, in only a few feet of water where underwater viewing requires nothing more than a snorkel and mask. When chummed during a moving tide that carries the smell of the fish scraps far and wide, the sharks are quick to respond. As the fish began appearing, Gary threw fish heads in front of me. The sharks swam up to take the food right in front of the camera, paying little attention to me or the other snorkelers. The only thing missing from the amazing encounter was the notorious bull sharks, which apparently leave the area in May and return in August, possibly to take advantage of the runs of tuna and bonito in deeper water offshore.

On my second trip to Walker's Cay with my family and Bill Boyce, we got our time with the bulls. It was early November, right after a period of rough weather, so we were the only guests and had the place to ourselves. We didn't waste any time getting into the water, and within three minutes the biggest of bulls had showed up looking for scraps. Gary affectionately called her "Bahama Mama." She weighed well over 500 pounds, round as a rum barrel, but smooth and graceful in the shallow water. With my daughter, Jessica, on my left and Bill on my right, we waited as Gary threw fish scraps in front of us. Soon we had more bulls and a pair of hefty lemon sharks in view. With cameras rolling, we were able to shoot some graphic close-ups. The most important part of this process was to keep still in the water so the sandy bottom would not get stirred up and the sharks would remain confident around us. A sudden movement would startle them, and when spooked, they would kick up silt on their way out. They always returned.

After an hour, we counted eight bulls and four lemons around us, providing an exhilarating experience and a close encounter to remember. The lemons were long and slim compared with the heavy-bodied bulls, and they would swim in close to pull fish scraps off the tops of rocks barely covered by water. In the middle of all this, a spotted moray eel grabbed two fingers on my left hand as I held onto a rock, trying to steady myself as I photographed a bull right in front of me. Talk about being surprised! Since the wound was bleeding profusely, it seemed like a good time to end the shoot. On shore, Gary sterilized the cut and scolded me for not wearing gloves. The moray's teeth had pierced through the fingernail. Despite my injury, Jessica had enjoyed the interaction with the big sharks, so we repeated the feed the following afternoon in better light conditions. This time I wore gloves.

Returning in May, 2001, I joined a group of 16 students from Nova Southwestern University's Oceanographic Center, who were taking a shark ecology field trip under the supervision of Dr. Erich Ritter and Dr. Mahmood Shivji. On one afternoon about 20

Below: Gary Adkinson, along with daughter Brittany and wife Brenda, has used the Walker's Cay shark population to educate thousands of visitors on shark ecology and behavior.

Above: Alexander and Jessica Harvey on their way to the Shark Rodeo.

Opposite: Reef Prowler, *acrylic on canvas. A Caribbean reef shark surrounded by blue runners is a frequent sight on Bahamian reefs.*

Bulls and Tarpon, *acrylic on canvas.*
A pair of bull sharks ambushes a school of
tarpon on a Bahamas flat.

people were standing on the rocky shoreline, watching as a few blacktips, lemons and nurse sharks consumed the fish scraps Gary had thrown in. The bull sharks had recently migrated, so we did not expect to see any big stuff. Suddenly a large black shadow came tearing in from the left, and a tall dorsal fin cleaved the surface. The dorsal was so tall, the image of an orca whale popped into my mind. The 11-foot-long animal turned toward us, allowing us to see it was a hammerhead shark of healthy dimensions. Eric and Gary were ecstatic.

I went in and filmed her for 30 minutes, getting precious close-up footage of her feeding. The snorkeling students did not spook her at all, and she methodically sucked up many carcasses that Gary threw 3 feet from me, in view of the camera. She had a large, plump belly, leading Erich and Gary to believe she was going to drop her pups shortly. During this encounter she paid no attention to the other sharks, but I wondered what might have transpired if some bull sharks had been present. This was my first

time swimming with a great hammerhead in a controlled situation, and I look forward to committing the incredible encounter to canvas.

Gary, Brenda and Barry have dedicated their lives to preserving the precious marine resources around Walker's Cay, and most of all, they want to share them with other people. In the last decade, thousands of divers have returned from the Walker's Cay Shark Rodeo with dramatically altered attitudes toward sharks. This experience, along with lectures and factual television documentaries, help the Walker's Cay team educate the public about the shark's biology and ecology and discredit the sensationalist garbage that so often portrays these sea creatures as mindless killers.

At the time of this writing in late 2001, Gary was in negotiations with the Bahamian government to have an area north of Walker's Cay stretching toward Matanilla Reef designated as a marine park. If this happens, all marine life in the area will benefit from the protection, none more so than the fascinating sharks of Walker's Cay.

CHAPTER 5

FLORIDA
A Foundation for Business

Although I've been traveling to Florida for many years, I have spent very little time fishing and diving there. Mostly I attend art shows, boat shows and tournament exhibits, make public appearances, help with charity fund-raisers and do administrative work associated with running my business. I also spend a great deal of time there working for various conservation groups, particularly the International Game Fish Association for which I have served as a board member since 1993.

I have missed out on a lot of great fishing opportunities because of the work commitments, but I have occasionally gotten away from it all and wet a line for tarpon, snook, redfish, sailfish or kingfish. None of these encounters has ever been particularly dramatic, but they don't always need to be exceptional to inspire new artwork.

One really magical encounter took place at a spot called Robby's Place, just south of Islamorada in the Florida Keys. Raleigh Werking took me there one sunny morning on an incoming tide. I jumped into the water while he fed the local tarpon. The fish proved quite indifferent to my presence, eating the scraps right in front of me. This allowed for close study, and a number of paintings have come out of this one visit.

Similarly, fishing with Scott Boyd for snook and redfish in Chuckoloskee or off Jupiter Inlet with Charlie Forman during the full moon in May for kingfish proved great experiences that I later translated into paintings. These opportunities have allowed me to capture the flavor and mood of the species involved.

Encounters with manatees are always special. I dived with a lot of them in Jamaica, most often in rivers but a few times in the sea. However, I seldom had the opportunity to interact with them the way I did recently in Homosassa Springs and Crystal River on Florida's west coast. The manatee refuge in Homosassa offers the best place to get close to manatees, and the water is clear and full of fish such as jack crevalle, snook, redfish, mullet, sheepshead, catfish, alligator gar and gray snapper.

Experiencing this kind of diversity at one location allows me to include a lot more color and variety in a manatee painting, creating more interest, movement and drama.

Above: Rivermates, *acrylic on canvas, a piece which Harvey painted in his Cayman Islands studio (opposite).*

Left: Guy snorkels with a manatee in Florida's Homosassa River. Photo by Wyland.

Alone, a manatee is monochromatic and bland, so I feel I can portray a lot more by including their river mates.

I joined fellow marine artist Wyland on my last trip to Homosassa River in November 2000, and we spent two mornings interacting with the manatees before going to paint a mural on the wall of Florida's State Wildlife Parks administrative building. Wyland very kindly invited me to collaborate on this wall with him, and he followed that up by including me on his next wall in Marathon, in the Florida Keys, in February 2001.

Wyland is the world's best-known marine artist. He has contributed more to the education of the general public about marine environmental issues than any other artist. His use of huge public murals has been an effective tool in bringing the beauty of marine life, particularly marine mammals, into people's lives around the world.

One of the most interesting projects I have undertaken in Florida was the sinking of a ship to create an artificial reef as part of the Broward County Artificial Reef Program. Patti Carr and the Pompano Beach Fishing Rodeo organized the project. Each year, they purchase a derelict vessel, clean it up and make it "diver safe" before they sink it in a specific location near several other wrecks. In 1997, I sponsored the preparation and sinking of a 180-foot freighter. Part of the preparation involved my painting fish silhouettes along the side of the ship. I received a great deal of help from a variety of people, including my children, Jessica and Alexander.

Above: Snook in Mangroves, *mixed media.*

Opposite: Bull Dolphin, *watercolor.*

Below: Alexander and Jessica give Dad a lesson in painting on the Guy Harvey Reef, a ship sunk off the coast of Fort Lauderdale as part of the Pompano Beach Fishing Rodeo's artificial reef project.

Above: Marine artists Wyland and Guy Harvey work together on a mural in Homosassa, Florida.

Left: Guy Harvey Reef, mixed media.

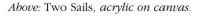

Above: Two Sails, *acrylic on canvas.*

Right: Silver Kings, *acrylic on canvas.*

We sunk the ship on May 10, 1997, in 140 feet of water and named it the Guy Harvey Reef. The superstructure sits at 90 feet and is easily accessed by divers. On subsequent visits, I've been pleased to find the wreck has quickly become home to a number of large barracuda, jacks, angelfish, grunts and snappers.

My most recent project — the Guy Harvey Research Institute, inaugurated in January 2000 — resulted from my scientific background and interests, and from Charlie Forman, who first proposed its formation. Directed by Dr. Richard Dodge, Dr. Richard Speiler and Dr. Mahmood Shivji and based out of Nova Southeastern University's Oceanographic Center in Fort Lauderdale, the GHRI provides global-level leadership in the generation of the scientific data necessary to conserve the world's fish resources. These resources are experiencing an unprecedented assault from exploitation, pollution

and habitat loss associated with an explosive growth in human populations. Most acknowledge that effective conservation and management measures are urgently needed to halt and reverse the trend.

Sound scientific information forms the basis of effective conservation and management decisions. As its core mission, the GHRI focuses on the performance of high-quality, solution-orientated scientific research needed to build that foundation. The institute's ultimate goal: the conservation, restoration, enhancement and increased understanding of the world's marine resources. GHRI will provide advanced training to students from the U.S. and other countries, who will serve as the future stewards of the health of our oceans.

Financial support for GHRI research comes partly from the Guy Harvey Inc. licensing program, as well as from private donations.

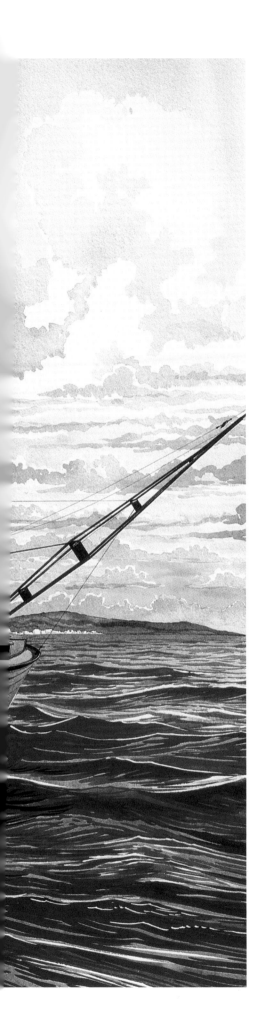

CHAPTER 6

Opposite: Havana Hookup, *watercolor.*
This piece was donated to the International
Game Fish Association auction in 1994.

CUBA
In Hemingway's Shadow

H*e was an old man who fished alone in a skiff in the Gulf Stream and had gone eighty-four days now without taking a fish."*
Well, you know what happened next.

Following in the footsteps of Ernest Hemingway, I first went to Havana in May 1989 at the invitation of Armando Ferrat from Cancún, Mexico. We were participating in the annual Ernest Hemingway Billfish Tournament at the Hemingway Marina, along with several teams from Mexico, Canada, Germany, Italy and South America. I was impressed with the level of organization, the social events and the Cubans' enthusiasm for fishing. Unfortunately, the action was very slow, but I did have the opportunity to fish with Manuel Bell, who had fished a great deal with Hemingway in his later years. The hours went by quickly, and while watching the skipping baits, he told stories about the famous author's fishing exploits and his landside antics.

The main reason I had taken this trip was to have an opportunity to visit Hemingway's house, Finca Vigia — now a museum — in San Francisco de Paula, a town outside Havana. Though tourists aren't allowed inside the impressively large yet simple house, Armando arranged for special permission from the curator for the two of us to walk through the premises. Once inside, I got a strange feeling of unusual well-being — and no, it was not the Cuban rum. I rarely get mushy at big events or movies, but I was charged with emotion inside Finca Vigia.

After the tour, I presented the curator and the Museo Ernest Hemingway with one of the 12-part limited-edition series of black-and-white prints I had done from *The Old Man and the Sea* so many years before.

The following day we went to see Hemingway's old skipper, Gregorio Fuentes, at his home in the small village of Cojimar, just east of Havana. I spent two hours listening to Gregorio, then 92 years old, tell stories of the old days spent fishing with Hemingway while Armando interpreted for me. Later, we all went for lunch in the beachfront cantina featured in the original story. Sitting on the terrace sipping a beer, I could imagine the fishermen 50 years ago discussing the day's fishing and the baseball results in the American League.

Fishing was always my primary hobby when growing up in Jamaica, so the story of Santiago catching the giant blue marlin off Havana was definitely a favorite. In fact, during my first year at Aberdeen University in Scotland, I spent most of my free time

Right: Harvey presents a copy of Santiago's Finest Hour *to Gregorio Fuentes, Hemingway's long-time skipper who died at the age of 104 in January 2002.*

Opposite: Harvey selected 60 pen-and-ink drawings from his Old Man *series to illustrate* Santiago's Finest Hour, *a book produced to commemorate Hemingway's legacy and benefit the IGFA.*

Below: Museum curator and Armando Ferrat provide a tour of "Finca Vigia" in May 1989.

working on a series of pen-and-ink illustrations of this famous story. I began with all the action sequences — the fish jumping, the killing of the fish and the battle against the sharks. Gradually, I rounded out the story and finally published the first set of limited-edition prints in 1985. The 100 sets of 12 prints sold out. Following my Havana trip, I was so inspired that I revised some of this work and added more to the series, increasing the total number of illustrations from 44 to 70.

My second trip to Cuba, in May 1994, took me to Santiago in the southeast to fish in a tournament with some other Jamaican participants. Santiago is only 110 miles north of Port Antonio, Jamaica, so boats often traveled back and forth between the two countries. The event was memorable: Several blues and a white marlin were caught.

In 1999, the International Game Fish Association, which Hemingway served as founding vice-president in 1939, celebrated his centennial year with an exhibition of some artifacts on loan from Danilo Arrate, present curator of the Museo Ernest Hemingway. In conjunction, Raleigh Werking and I released the book *Santiago's Finest Hour* featuring my 60 best pen-and-ink illustrations to commemorate Hemingway's legacy and to benefit the IGFA. I obtained permission from the Hemingway Estate and his publishers, Scribner's of New York, to reproduce excerpts of the original story as captions for my illustrations.

Later that year, I was asked to make a presentation at an international literary forum, or colloquium, in Havana celebrating Ernest Hemingway's life and times. On the afternoon of the first day of the forum, Gregorio Fuentes came in and sat through the session. Here, I presented him with a personalized copy of *Santiago's Finest Hour.* He proceeded to look through the entire book in the two hours that he sat there, not appearing to be interested in the proceedings at all! He kindly signed a copy of the book for my personal collection. At 102 years old, he appeared very fit, healthy and totally cognizant of all that was going on around him. I regretted not being able to speak Spanish and so converse with him, but we parted without the need to say anything more.

I also presented copies of the book to the local libraries and the Museo Ernest Hemingway, as well as to the Ambos Mundos Hotel, where we stayed. Hemingway spent a lot of time in that hotel's room 511, which has been preserved as it was when he stayed there.

Left: The fully restored Pilar *rests on blocks at Museo Ernest Hemingway. Photo by Raleigh Werking.*

Opposite: Havana Hook Up II, *watercolor. The piece has proven a successful T-shirt image.*

Below: Harvey at the helm of the Pilar *in Havana. Photo by Raleigh Werking.*

We visited the Museo the next day, and once again we were allowed to walk through Finca Vigia. In fact, this time the entire staff came out to meet us and give us the tour. The furniture, books, animal mounts and carpets were in excellent condition and have been preserved exactly as they were during the 22 years he lived there. The house still presents a fleeting glimpse of the author's life and remains filled with a sense of his presence. The feeling of exhilaration I had first experienced in 1989 returned.

Following the house tour, we moved through the garden, past the big empty pool, to the final resting place of the *Pilar*. She was a twin-engine 42-foot Wheeler, a state-of-the-art sport-fishing boat built of wood. Hemingway purchased her in 1934 and fished on her for 25 years. The *Pilar* was being refurbished during my visit 10 years before, so I never had an opportunity to see her, let alone go on board. Besides, she resides on blocks, undercover, and is surrounded by a raised walkway; no one is allowed aboard.

On this trip, however, Danilo let us go aboard after removing our shoes. I took a lot of photographs of the detail of the boat. As I do a lot of paintings of Hemingway in action, this was invaluable reference for me. One thing I noticed was that the renovated *Pilar* had a single shaft, propeller and rudder, and yet the boat started out as a twin-engine vessel. Hemingway must have converted her later on for some reason. Also, she has a high transom and a low gunwale. Hemingway liked to fight marlin standing up — the same way he wrote. The low gunwale, however, would have made catching fish somewhat tricky in all but calm seas, unless he resorted to using the fighting chair when it got windy. All that's missing on the boat today are the outriggers.

Our visit to Havana included a tour of the El Morro castle, lighthouse and the army barracks at the harbor entrance. The fortifications are as massive as they are extensive, and the heavy artillery still sits in position, although rusty with neglect. Likewise, most of the quarters can be described as derelict. I don't think Hemingway would be very happy with the conditions in the Havana of 2000 — 40 years after he passed on. Still, the Spanish architecture is durable and imposing, in spite of the lack of care, and Old Havana remains an absolute cultural paradise.

CHAPTER 7

CAYMAN ISLANDS
At Home in Las Tortugas

No records exist to indicate the Cayman Islands were inhabited prior to Christopher Columbus' fourth voyage to the New World in 1503. He named the territory Las Tortugas because of the abundance of sea turtles on and around the three islands. In 1655 the English, under Oliver Cromwell, captured Jamaica from the Spanish, and in 1670 the territory was declared British property under the Treaty of Madrid.

Legend has it that the islands' first settlers were deserters from Oliver Cromwell's army, but no proof exists to support this. What is known: In 1668 an attempt was made to settle Little Cayman and Cayman Brac, but the settlers were soon recalled to Jamaica because they could not be protected from Spanish pirates. In those days, the Cayman Islands played a large role in the piracy that gripped the Caribbean. They were remote and had plenty of turtle meat and water to support famous characters such as Henry Morgan and Edward Teach, who used the islands as a safe haven. It was not until the 1730s that the islands' first permanent settlers were recorded.

The Harvey family migrated to the Cayman Islands in August 1999, leaving behind more than three centuries of family history in Jamaica. We were now a statistic, along with 2 million other Jamaicans who had departed since 1962. More than half of Jamaica's current population have never known a pre-Manley Jamaica, and so have never experienced life without deprivation and brutality. Life today in the British colony of the Cayman Islands reminds me a great deal of life in Jamaica in the 1960s.

I can safely make this comparison because of the strong historical influence Jamaica has had over the Caymans. Today, several thousand Jamaicans live and work there and have brought with them a strong, positive cultural influence in food, music and lifestyle. Along with the Jamaicans, British, European and American residents actually outnumber the Caymanians — most work in the banking, hotel and diving businesses. Cayman enjoys a high standard of living with little unemployment, good infrastructure and a well-educated population that for the most part is law-abiding, friendly and courteous. The cost of living is high because everything has to be imported; nothing is grown on the islands.

Above: Jessica Harvey interacts with a hawksbill turtle along Grand Cayman's North Wall.

Opposite: Turtle Collage, *watercolor.*

Above: Jessica and friends at The Sandbar in North Sound, Grand Cayman. The plentiful and playful rays have made this location among the most visited dive sites in the world.

Compared with Jamaica, Cayman has few natural resources; even fresh water has to be made from desalinated seawater. Its primary resource can be found in its nearshore reefs, which serve as a major source of tourism income, thanks to aggressive protection and marketing to North American divers. However, as the population on the island of Grand Cayman has grown in the past two decades, and as foreign investment has poured into Cayman, the increased development has led to mangrove depletion and an increase in solid and liquid waste. Studies suggest that algae growth is beginning to smother the coral on some shallow reef systems, most notably those close to the capital, George Town, and adjacent to Seven Mile Beach.

Still, the diving in all three Cayman Islands remains superb, with excellent visibility, tremendous fish and reef life, warm water and little current. It has been a wonderful asset for me to have on my doorstep; I dive most weekends and have worked diligently here to increase my photography skills. My diving buddy nowadays is my daughter, Jessica, who is already an experienced diver. Some of our favorite sites include the wreck of the *Oro Verde*, Orange Canyon, Tarpon Alley and Rum Point. All along the reef wall we experience frequent encounters with eagle rays, turtles, tarpon, big snappers and groupers, barracudas and countless parrotfish, angelfish and other small species. Mooring buoys mark dive sites all around the islands, so anchoring is unnecessary, preventing damage to the coral. Many parts of the islands' reef systems

*The reefs surrounding the Cayman Islands
allow ample opportunity for practicing
underwater photography skills. Top to bottom:
Female hogfish, queen angelfish, mutton
snapper and male hogfish.*

71

are protected from fishing. In these spots, the fish become conditioned to the presence of divers, which really helps when trying to work with them.

We frequently visit "The Sandbar" in North Sound, a spot famous for holding the world's largest aggregation of southern stingrays, *Dasyatis americana*. Here the rays gather on a sandbar in shallow water that is protected from the northeasterly surge by the fringing reef. In "Stingray City," 2 miles to the west, rays gather in deeper water, and scuba gear must be used for the best encounter. Stingrays first began congregating there as far back as the 1950s when fishermen cleaned their catch. By the mid-'80s, dive operators were hand-feeding the rays, which quickly became conditioned to the divers and showed up daily to feed. Annually since then, tens of thousands of swimmers, snorkelers and divers have enjoyed the thrill of interacting with these wild animals, making these sites among the most visited dive sites in the world.

According to local dive operators, the number of rays has increased during the past decade, but no one can say scientifically how the long-term interaction with humans has affected the ray population. Little is known about the life history of these animals. Sharks, particularly the great hammerhead, are their only predators. Local fishermen sometimes catch rays by accident, but there is no demand for their meat. Allocation of this resource, therefore, is not a contentious issue.

The ray experience has become synonymous with the Cayman Islands, so much so that the image of the stingray is as prominent now as that of the turtle.

For centuries, mariners knew the Caymans as Las Tortugas. They came here to catch live turtles that would serve as fresh meat during their long voyages. The Cayman turtle population suffered greatly from this exploitation, but a turtle farm was set up in North Sound in 1968 to replenish natural stocks and to supply local demand for turtle products. The farm moved to its present location in West Bay in 1971, and by 1978 had achieved its objective of having sufficient brood stock — around 350 adult green turtles — to make the farm self-sufficient and economically viable. The farm rears around 8,000 turtles annually for its commercial commitments and products.

The government of the Cayman Islands has owned and operated the Cayman Turtle Farm since 1983. Besides ranking as one of the main tourist attractions in Cayman, the farm operates as a well-respected research facility that concentrates on breeding programs to help recolonize the ocean with turtles. So far, approximately 30,000 animals have been released into the sea. All have been tagged for scientific purposes, and migration information and tag returns have flooded in from all over the Caribbean. I encounter hawksbill and green turtles on nearly every dive in Cayman.

Above: Alexander Harvey tours the Grand Cayman Turtle Farm.

As with most other governments in the Caribbean, the Cayman Islands have yet to appreciate the true value of a living shark as a tourist attraction. Sharks grow slowly and live long lives, so their protection from exploitation is now vital throughout the world. One way of protecting them and benefiting economically from them at the same time is to facilitate shark ecotourism. Yet the acceptance of shark feeding has been slower in Cayman than in the Bahamas, where numerous opportunities are available. This is partly because of the relatively small area of shallow water around the islands that could support a population of coastal shark species, as well as a lack of support from local fishing and diving interests. However, one East End operator, Ocean Frontiers, has successfully attracted a dozen Caribbean reef sharks to a shallow site, using a safe system based on the one Gary Adkinson developed in Walker's Cay. Divers are treated to a two-hour course on shark biology and ecology before entering the water to see them. In January 2002, the Cayman Islands government banned the feeding of sharks.

The Caymans have been more open to sport fishing, which took off in the late 1970s with the Rotary Club Tournaments initiated by Capt. Theo Bodden. The Cayman Airways Pilots Tournament, organized in 1980 by a Jamaican, Capt. Robby Hamaty, marked the

Above: Jessica dives with the residents of "Tarpon Alley" along Grand Cayman's North Wall.

first international fishing contest there. Anglers caught marlin all around the island and out at the Twelve Mile Bank, where yellowfin tuna and wahoo are seasonally abundant. Nowadays, anglers go farther offshore to Sixty Mile Bank and Pickle Bank, 90 miles away toward the Cuban coast.

The Cayman Islands Angling Club was formed in 1982, and in 1983 Bill Rewalt collected from the small charter fleet catch statistics that indicated an abundance of blue marlin year round. Realizing the potential in sport-fishing tourism, the government, under the leadership of the late James Bodden, promoted a month-long fishing extravaganza offering $1 million in prize money to the angler breaking the Cayman blue marlin record of 584 pounds. Rewalt ran the event through the whole of June each year and attracted a great deal of overseas participation, putting Cayman on the Caribbean sport-fishing map.

In the years to come, only two blues over 500 pounds were boated during the Million Dollar Month event, but they did not reach the magical $1 million mark. The event was replaced in 1998 by the Cayman Islands International Tournament, headed by Horace DuQuesnay and held in late April. Thanks to a minimum qualifying weight of 300 pounds, all 90 blue marlin caught in this event over the past two years have been released.

Ironically, the Caymans — and not my home island of Jamaica — is where I turned in my first blue marlin release, in June of 1984. It was during a Cayman Island Angling Club event, which had switched to a release format several years before Jamaica would adopt the more progressive rules.

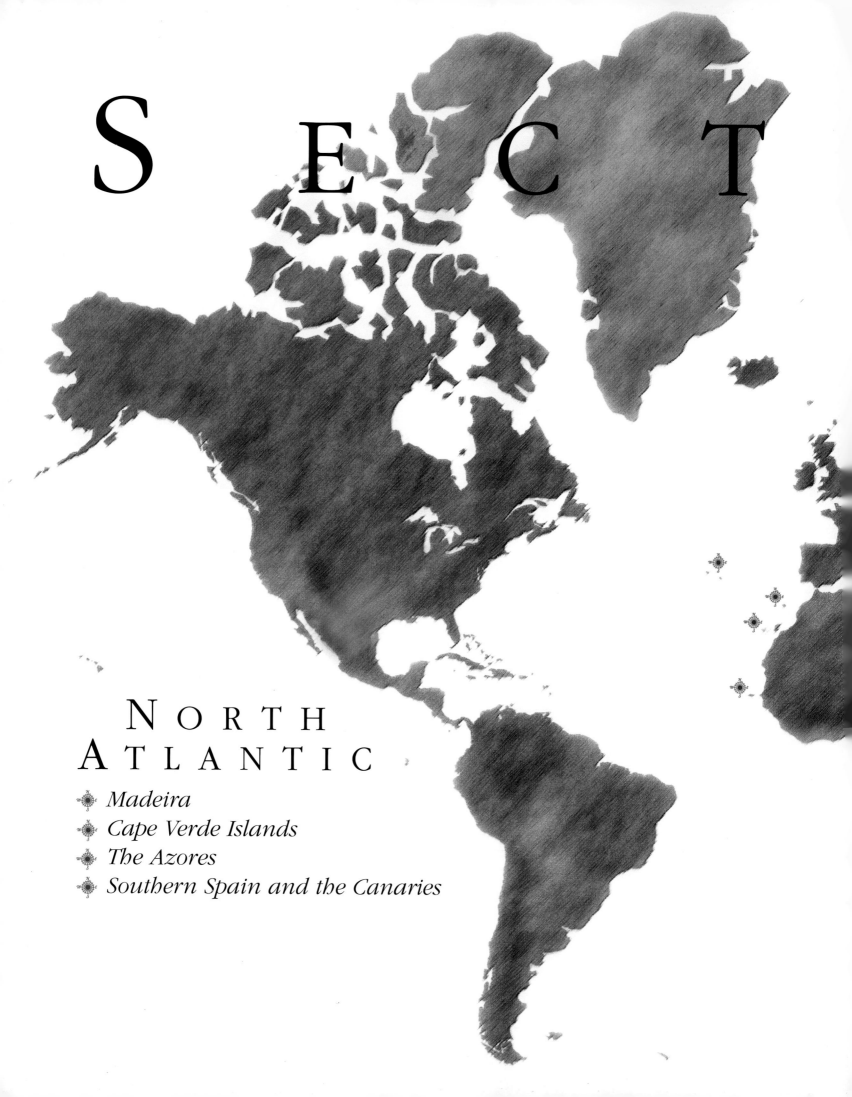

S E C T

I O N 2

CHAPTER 8

MADEIRA
Battles with Monster Blues

R ight long!" I said firmly to Charles "C.P." Perry, who sat next to me aboard *Chunda* — Stewart Campbell's Garlington Express 44 — as we trolled a few miles off Madeira's south coast. C.P. and Marty Snow sprang into action as Capt. Barkey Garnsey calmly directed the show from the tower, his voice coming through a cockpit speaker system.

The massive blue marlin charged the right long teaser again as C.P. reeled it toward the boat. "Get ready, Stewart. It's a nice fish ... but not big enough. Throw the 80-pound." Stewart sent out the rigged mackerel as the teasers came in. I shot a nice photo as the fish crossed the wake and nailed the left long lure in a flurry of spray. Marty teased the fish closer; the shadow appeared huge in the foam. I'd never seen such a large fish so close. It missed the mackerel on the first attempt, then spun around and ate it. Stewart gave a short, four-second drop-back. The hand-off went smoothly, and we were now tight on a typical Madeira blue of 800 pounds. Hooking a fish of this size would have made headlines anywhere else in the world. Here, it was just another day at the office for *Chunda's* crew.

Stewart made short work of the fish, bringing it close to the boat in a matter of minutes. I got my underwater camera ready, put on my dive gear and prepared to jump in as C.P. took the first wrap on the leader. I sat on the covering board and hesitated, looking down at the lit-up, 14-foot marlin beneath me. Barkey's authoritative voice came over the speakers: "There's your fish, Guy. What do you want to do now?"

As if waiting for the cue, the marlin did a 180 and took off. C.P. dumped the leader, and the fish headed for the horizon. I floundered around the cockpit in my dive gear and long fins, trying to grab my topside camera (knocking over Miss Nikki, Stewart's wife, in the process) as the fish continued its dramatic display. The marlin's tail tore up the calm ocean, then the furious blue turned back toward the boat, approaching like an Exocet missile. I quickly reached for the camera and fired off a roll of film as the marlin overtook the boat and shot around the bow. In spite of Barkey's expertise, the

Above: The picturesque south coast of Madeira, where anglers often troll for blue marlin just offshore.

Opposite: Jumping Blue Off Cabo Joao, *watercolor.*

Above: An 800-pound blue shifts gears during an exciting fight aboard Chunda *off the Madeira coast.*

double line caught and broke on the teaser reel in the leg of the tower. Yow!

We all wore smiles when the smoke cleared, even though the fish had escaped. The energetic blue had put on a spectacular jumping demonstration, and we managed to get some of it on film.

This was Stewart Campbell's second season in Madeira, and he and his unique team were record hunting. The previous year, Stewart had weighed two blues over the magical mark of 1,000 pounds and came close to beating the existing 80-pound line-class world record of 1,189 pounds. Stewart and the *Chunda* team employ the bait-and-switch method, which allows Capt. Barkey to judge the size of a marlin in the spread before instructing Stewart on which tackle to use. To break the existing 30-pound-test record (840 pounds), Stewart needed a marlin of 850 to 1,100 pounds. If a real monster of 1,200-plus pounds came up, Stewart would pitch a bait on 80-pound gear for that record. And if a smaller fish (below 800) showed, the crew used 80-pound test, often letting a guest hook and fight the fish for tag-and-release.

Not two hours after that explosive fish's visit, another big blue slid up next to the right long teaser.

"Right long!" I cried. C.P. reeled in the teaser as Stewart got ready.

"OK, Stewart, this is a nice fish. Get the 30-pound," Barkey coached. "Hold it there ... she's right on you ... she's going to eat!"

Having gulped the mackerel, the marlin kept swimming toward the boat and crossed the wake to charge the left short teaser. Seeing the full length of the fish, I felt simply astounded. How could Stewart set out to catch such a huge fish on 30-pound test?

But catch it he did, after three hours and five minutes — one of the longest fights Stewart has endured on 30-pound tackle. The fish jumped a great deal, often coming entirely out of the water, but many jumps were far away and out of range of my 210mm lens.

The crew boated the 872-pounder, which qualified for a new world record. All this excitement occurred on August 29, 1995, giving me my first taste of the monsters of Madeira.

Discovered in the early 1400s, the mountainous island of Madeira served as a springboard to the Americas for Columbus. Towering peaks of over 4,000 feet hold numerous sources of fresh water, so colonization happened rapidly. Funchal, built up the side of a mountain, grew to a city of 300,000 with magnificent views in every direction. A trip around the island offers a great day of sight-seeing. The typically Portuguese architecture features cobblestone sidewalks and hanging flower baskets bursting with vibrant colors. It seems that every square inch of horizontal space is used to grow bananas or grapevines. Two accomplished experts (my wife, Gillian, and Nikki Campbell) attest to Funchal's wonderful shopping opportunities. Madeira caters to northern European tourists, so visitors find plenty of hotels and inexpensive restaurants offering delicious meals.

Sailboats choke the little marina in Funchal; visiting sport-fishing boats are lucky to find a slip from year to year. Very colorful, hand-painted logos of vessels from around the world decorate the marina walls.

Local charter boats begin fishing in May for bigeye tuna and usually find marlin by June if there is bait to be found around the island. The best blue marlin fishing normally occurs in late July and August.

My goal in Madeira was to film free-swimming, large blue marlin. Though I'd talked with Stewart at length about my experiences with sailfish and striped marlin at Cocos Island and black marlin in Australia, he remained unconvinced. He believed that a crew casting teasers or strip baits from a stopped boat could not entice blue marlin to stay around for long. I thought differently; unless we tried it, we'd never know.

The next day we raised three blues. The first hung back in the spread, a huge shadow that would not come to the teasers. Stewart let me hook the second fish, a 600-pounder, and I jumped it off after a minute. The third was smaller. It mauled every teaser but would not eat the mackerel pitch bait. How agonizing — I should have been in the water with this fish! It finally departed, unhooked and undocumented.

Having built up momentum and devised plans for a jump-in, we then went through a long, fishless dry patch of six days. Waves of blue marlin often come through Madeira, keeping anglers quite busy for a couple of days, and then the fish disappear for a couple of weeks. Other boats may pick up white marlin, a spearfish or two and some bigeye tuna, but Stewart goes every day with the crew, pulling teasers and waiting for that giant to show up in the spread.

On my last day of this trip, we enjoyed the illustrious company of Pierre Clostermann. Having been a World War II fighter-pilot ace, a minister of the Charles de Gaulle government in France and head of Cessna Aircraft Corp., Pierre is a reasonably famous person. He's also an author, an accomplished artist and a well-traveled angler. Above all, he shows a tremendous sense of humor.

While in preparatory school in England, at the tender age of 8, one of my favorite books was *The Big Show* by Clostermann. The autobiographical account details his Battle of Britain days, flying Hurricanes and Spitfires for the Royal Air Force. He became a war hero as the French pilot with the most confirmed kills.

Much later in life, I found out that Pierre served on the International Game Fish Association's board of trustees. I was awed when we were introduced at the annual IGFA auction in 1986. A famous statesman, businessman and renowned author — and he fishes! We became good friends over the years, swapping artwork, books and fishing stories.

Five minutes after putting teasers in the water (we'd left the marina in Funchal at the

Below: Stewart Campbell poses with his 872-pound blue marlin that set a line-class world record in the 30-pound-test category.

Above: Angler, author, pilot, businessman and friend: Pierre Clostermann.

crack of 10:30 a.m.), Pierre, Stewart and I were having an animated discussion about tarpon fishing in West Africa when a 700-pound blue marlin showed up.

"Left short!" came the sharp order from above. "Throw the 80-pound, Stewart," instructed Barkey. Stewart, always the gentleman, insisted that one of his guests catch the fish. Pierre and I argued back and forth for 30 seconds while Barkey struggled to keep the ravenous marlin from devouring the transom. Pierre finally sat down, exclaiming, "Voila, Monsieur Guy. I am already *trés fatigué* from our discussion, zee marleen is yours!"

The blue ate the mackerel and began a wonderful dance in front of the town of Funchal. Again, I made the wrong choice: I should have picked up the camera instead of the fishing rod. C.P. wired the fish in 20 minutes, and I added a Madeira blue to my list of catches. Then I put on my dive gear while Stewart hopped in the chair to control the tired fish. Barkey slowly drove the boat past me several times, and I was able to get some close-up shots of the magnificent marlin in very clear water. The fish swam off strongly on release.

Madeira's 1995 season ended shortly after my visit. Despite slow fishing compared with the previous year's, a couple of granders had been weighed. I couldn't wait to return.

Below: A 700-pound blue caught by Harvey about to be released.

Above: This 40-pound spearfish made a surprise appearance by attacking a large marlin lure.

I made my way back to Madeira on July 25, 1996 — one month after Stewart survived a harrowing incident where he was dragged over the transom — with my family in tow and looking forward to six days with the *Chunda* team. We raised an 800-pound blue on each of our first two days, but couldn't coax a bite. The other boats were catching a marlin here and there, but it took hard work to find fish.

On the 28th, we ran down to the western end of the island and fished near the wind line before trolling toward the landmark of Ribero Brava. A 700-pound blue came up on the long right teaser and followed it to the boat as C.P. and Spencer Stratton worked the teasers furiously. Stewart gave me a chance to hook the fish, but it remained intent on following the teaser, swimming right past the mackerel, then past the transom! I felt really cute, watching a rampaging marlin paddle alongside the cockpit, lit up like a Christmas tree, with my spurned bait splashing 20 feet behind it. We gawked at the fish for 30 seconds before it disappeared under the boat.

"Hold the mackerel in position," Stewart advised. "The marlin will turn outward and see the bait as it crosses the wake." Indeed, the fish turned to the left and crunched the left short teaser, then, with its back out of the water, took my mackerel as it departed. A spectacular bite! I caught the marlin in 20 minutes, handed the rod to Stewart and jumped in to shoot a long video of this frisky marlin before the crew turned her loose.

Not long afterward, Barkey called me to the tower. He pointed out huge white splashes on the surface a couple of miles away. "Only bluefin tuna make splashes that big," he said. "Let's wander over and take a look. If they're still going off when we get there, we'll put out a bait."

Having never caught a bluefin, I was anxious to see this. We eventually reached the spot, and sure enough, giants continued thrashing the school of bait. C.P. quickly hooked me up to an 80-pound outfit skipping a mackerel down the center. Barkey left all four teasers out as we trolled through the school — tuna to the left of us, tuna to the right, rolling on bait and boiling the surface. I regretted not dropping into the water, camera in hand, to record this bonanza, but a sudden explosion of spray engulfed the left short teaser and blew those thoughts out of my head. The teaser reel whined and groaned under the strain until the 200-pound mono snapped. Then it was Barkey's turn to whine: "He got Mr. T! He got Mr. T!"

Three other giants simultaneously crashed the left long, my mackerel and the right long. We scored a quadruple header of bluefin, though only one line had a hook, and I found myself attached to a marine freight train via 80-pound-test. Not long into the

fight, I snagged another line; C.P. pulled in 100 yards of 200-pound mono with "Mr. T," Barkey's favorite teaser, on the end. All smiles in the tower!

After an exciting 45 minutes, I thought I'd beaten the tuna that Barkey called 800-plus pounds. Catching a huge tuna in deep water on 80-pound would have been a satisfying personal angling achievement, but I broke the fish off close to the boat. Nonetheless, it was one of my most memorable experiences to have fought two of the ocean's greatest fish — a hefty blue marlin and a giant bluefin tuna — in the same day. Thank you, Stewart and Barkey, for providing this opportunity.

On Monday, July 29, we did not raise a fish until 3 p.m. I was in the tower chatting with Barkey when the fish came up, its blue tail flashing, in the middle of the spread. It dropped back to the left long teaser, and Spencer brought her closer, reeling on the teaser rod.

"This is a hot fish!" called Barkey. "Not big enough, Stewart. Throw the 80-pound!" Stewart kindly let me do the honors with a fish I should have dived on. It was all over the teasers, bite after crashing bite. I love teaser fishing because you get so many chances to see a marlin at its best, in its most aggressive mood. Again, the marlin swam past the boat on the right, went under and nailed the left short before turning on the mackerel in a blistering departing bite — the ultimate fly-fisherman's strike. I came tight on another beautiful 800-pound blue.

In a tough, 40-minute contest, the fish jumped repeatedly before settling down to a deep, dogging battle. C.P. finally touched the leader; I jumped out of the chair, into my

Above: Harvey completed this commission to commemorate Stewart Campbell's world-record 872-pound blue taken aboard Chunda.

*Above: The massive Madeira blues caught
by Campbell and photographed by Harvey
provided spectacular acrobatic displays.*

dive gear and over the side. We'd planned for C.P. to snorkel above me, with the tag stick in hand, and tag the marlin underwater. In perfect execution, C.P. dove 20 feet and planted the tag firmly in the left shoulder as the fish shot past me. I continued filming for a few more minutes until Spencer set her free, then followed her until I ran out of air.

In that clear water I could plainly see the benefit of giving marlin a short drop-back: Most fish are hooked in the mouth, with no bleeding, and leave carrying only a hook and short piece of leader. Circle hooks were just making their appearance in billfish angling at that time and would see extensive use by 2000.

By the end of this trip I had a good handle on the anatomy and proportions of the huge Madeira blues, which I conveyed in my paintings. These fish exhibit excellent condition, with small heads, short pectoral fins, very tall dorsal fins and stout bodies. They get so thick that their girth at the anal fin appears greater than at the shoulder. I verified this observation when measuring the girth at the anal fin of Stewart's 872-pound blue, finding it 3 inches greater than the shoulder girth. There is no body cavity at this point, only pure muscle that gives these big fish the ability to swim fast and jump high out of the water. Imagine the energy required to push 800 pounds of body 5 feet clear of the surface!

Precisely because of a sprinting marlin's power and speed, Stewart loosens the drag almost to free-spool to allow running marlin to take line easily without breaking it. He says experience helps an angler anticipate when fish will burst into a run. But once Stewart turns a fish's head, he exerts full drag and utilizes the line's maximum capacity.

Above: Harvey works on grander No. 1 of two on the Freed 'Em, *July 27, 1997. Photo by Kim Hensley.*

Nearly all the marlin caught in Madeira had been tagged with conventional spaghetti tags; the returns remained low, as expected. This system relies on the recapture and reporting of tagged fish. One blue that Stewart had tagged was recaptured not far away in the Canary Islands. And he caught one that had been tagged only two weeks earlier in Madeira by Capt. Kevin Nakamaru on *Pesca Grossa.* Yet another big blue was tagged, then recaptured a year later by the same boat, *Margarita*, with Capt. Roddy Hays at the helm.

The spaghetti tag's limitations center around the lack of information on where fish travel between tagging and recapture. In 1996, there was a lot of talk on the docks about trying to learn more about the movements and migrations of giant female blue marlin. Why do they come to Madeira? From where? Where do they go in the winter? Do they cross the Atlantic or go south along the West African coast? Stewart got together with two other concerned anglers, Don Tyson and Packy Offield, to sponsor the purchase and deployment of pop-up satellite tags on these big fish. They called on the expertise of Dr. Barbara Block, who had worked extensively with pop-up tags on Pacific blue marlin in Hawaii and bluefin tuna in the Atlantic.

The pop-up tag releases from fish after a predetermined time. This could be one, three, six or even 12 months. The tag breaks free from the fish at any depth, floats to the surface and transmits its position to a programmed satellite. In this way, researchers do not rely on recapturing the marlin. Additionally, one fish could bear two tags set to release three months apart, for example, providing a better idea of the course taken after release.

A more sophisticated and, therefore, more expensive generation of pop-up tag, called the archival tag, records location, water depth, water temperature and speed of the host marlin. One or two successful returns from archival tags may provide more information on migrations of nomadic marlin than all the conventional tags ever will.

After a great deal of anticipation, not to mention considerable investment of time, money and effort, the 1997 season in Madeira turned out to be disappointingly slow. Stewart and team, with Barbara Block on board, went 20 days without a marlin. The same was true for Peter Wright and Jim Huddleston on *Duyfken.* I scheduled 16 days

(July 22 to August 7) in Madeira to film the tagging of marlin with pop-up tags. I had been invited to go out on a number of different boats, and spent the first four days on *Can't Touch Dis*, a beautiful new 75-foot Merritt owned by my longtime Jamaican friend, Donna Robinson, and her husband, Jim. Donna caught a white marlin on the first day. I relished the chance to get in the clear water and followed the fish into the depths after its release. We had no bites for the next three days, and the entire fleet of 10 boats tallied only one or two bites per day. Some days no one raised a fish. With bait scarce, conditions did not look good for the scientists and anglers.

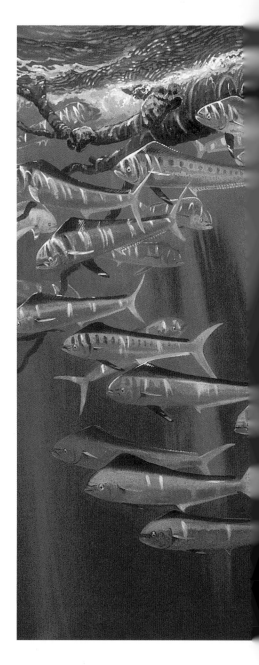

On July 26, Gillian and I went out on *Chunda* with Stewart and the gang. We enjoyed a lovely day trolling around the flat-calm seas with birds everywhere. We raised several white marlin on the teasers, but no blues. I caught up on research news with Barbara, as the Tag-A-Giant bluefin study, based in Hatteras, North Carolina, had been going well for a couple of seasons. In the evening, I made arrangements with Clay Hensley to fish on the *Freed 'Em* the following day, instead of the 28th as we'd previously scheduled. Strange how such a simple adjustment ends up changing your life.

On July 27, Gillian had to fly home to Jamaica and relieve Grandma of Jessica and Alexander. I took her to the airport in Funchal and saw her off on her long journey, then hustled back to the marina by 11:30 a.m. *Freed 'Em* left at 11:45 with Mikey Latham at the helm, who decided to troll out toward the Desertas. Three other boats in the same area had reported lots of activity, with birds, white marlin, tuna and a couple of blue marlin bites.

Mikey and Clay pull four teasers for bait-and-switch fishing, but also deploy a small hooked lure on a 30-pound rig as a stinger, far back down the middle. I was watching the lures, but glare on the water made it difficult to see them well. At 12:40 p.m. the very tip of a fin showed behind the long left. It looked like a little white marlin sneaking up on the teaser. I quickly reeled up the lure on the 30-pound outfit and said, "White on the long left!"

Nothing happened, nothing showed. Nobody else had seen the fish. Suddenly, a huge dorsal fin and shoulders loomed over the long right teaser. The lure disappeared in a massive boil.

As you can imagine, I felt like an idiot for shouting "white marlin." The biggest blue marlin I'd ever seen was chowing down on a Mold Craft Super Plunger behind the boat! Clay reeled in the long right while Aussie mate, Will, stood by on the left. I had the mackerel out in a flash on an 80-pound outfit, and I'd be lying if I said my knees were not shaking.

The great fish followed the teaser to the transom, where it stayed for a few seconds, looking at my skipping mackerel. Not a word was spoken. The marlin was huge and black, looking like an F16 fighter behind the little *Freed 'Em*. Then the fish stroked forward, its bill broke the surface behind the mackerel and the bait disappeared into the ominous shadow.

Line peeled off the 80SW Penn International as I jumped into the chair and buckled up. All was quiet for a while, and we maneuvered around, trying to get the marlin to do something. We heard on the radio that Kevin on *Pesca Grossa* had also hooked up off Cabo João, a few miles to the west.

The great marlin decided to make a move, and I backed the drag off as Stewart had taught me. The fish began a series of jumps, but I couldn't see much because Mikey had turned the boat to chase the fish as it headed toward the Canaries. When we got close, Mikey spun the boat, and I could see her: big, long, fat and jumping hard. To my dismay, the bait was clearly visible and flopping around her head. I had foul-hooked a fish in the 1,000-pound range. This was going to be a long haul on 80-pound line!

After a while, the fish settled to a straight pull near the surface, heading south. Mikey backed down until we could clearly see the fish and the double line came out of the water. Lit up in bright blue from bill to tail, the marlin glowed like a 15-foot fluorescent bulb. I asked Will to try to get some underwater shots of this, as my camera was ready to go. Will leaned over the transom and held the camera for three minutes with the *Freed 'Em* backing down. He did a remarkable job as it turned out, considering the strain on his arms from the force of the water. Its great tail oscillating sideways, pectorals spread wide like wings, the fish appeared ghostly, pale blue against the dark-blue background of the ocean.

After an hour of maneuvering and pulling from different angles, I got the double line on the reel a couple of times. Clay got ready to take the leader, and Will prepared to jump into the chair so I could dive with the fish.

Then the marlin began to jump again, going fast down-sea, showing how much energy she still had. She repeatedly climbed clear out of the water — all 15 feet of glistening predator — powerful, purposeful and shaking her great head. We then realized she was over the magic number. This was a grander!

Above: Grande, *acrylic on canvas.*

Above: Blue on Dorados, *watercolor.*

Opposite: A Madeira blue marlin carries a pop-up satellite tag prior to release aboard the Duyfken.

Clay got the leader after an hour and a quarter. Will and I made the switch, and I went into the water, face to face with "Big Julie." She lay on her side, tired, tail beating against the pull from Clay above. I could now see that the leader was wrapped twice around her bill, and the hook was embedded in the skin of her shoulder, below the dorsal fin. I had been lucky. The fish had thrown a couple of loops of leader around her bill during her valiant efforts to jump free, affording good leverage on her head and helping the hook stay buried.

Mikey led the marlin around me twice more before I called for the release. Will and Clay unwrapped the leader and cut it a couple of feet from the hook; the fish swam away, tilting to one side. I quickly swam up, the camera running, grabbed her dorsal fin with my free hand and rolled her over so she became upright. She started to kick as I hung on with my left hand, reaching for her left pectoral fin, anything to hold on to! I clutched her body with both arms extended and could not get my arms around

her massive circumference. I stayed with her as we slowly paddled into the blue. Out of the left corner of her mouth hung a foot of mono leader, the end cut by a knife. The eye of the hook was visible. This splendid fish had been caught before and released. But the only tag in her was ours. I was running out of air at 50 feet and let her go. Her great tail weaving slowly from side to side, she was tired but in great shape and had lost no blood. I watched as she slowly disappeared from view.

Stewart was 26 miles away, too far to come and plant a pop-up tag in our marlin. In the meantime, Kevin Nakamaru and his angler released a blue estimated at over 950 pounds.

We got straightened out, I dried off and we deployed the teasers again. Clay passed around the beer to celebrate as Mikey drove toward our original hookup position. We had abandoned the idea of trolling over to the Desertas, as it was now 2:15 p.m. and the wind had picked up.

I hadn't even finished my beer when Mikey yelled from above, "Right short! There's a slob on the right short!"

The big pink-and-white Mold Craft Super Plunger had disappeared inside the marlin's mouth. I dropped the mackerel into position as Mikey fought to get the teaser away from the marlin. The hot blue instantly swallowed the mackerel and then crashed the left short teaser. I reeled frantically, winding tight on the fish with the double line still on the reel. The fish jumped away from the boat, and Mikey said, "That's another big fish, Guy — as big as the first one!"

She charged off to the left in a greyhounding semicircle before settling down to what became a long, hard slog. Mikey worked hard as the fish pulled the little boat one way and the wind pushed it the other. We called the *Chunda* to get their team over with a pop-up tag.

After an hour we held the fish close enough to see it most of the time, and gained more ground after an hour and a half, with the double line staying on the reel. Then the fish began a tremendous series of jumps at the transom. At that point, I wanted to get out of the chair and behind my camera! The marlin took off again and ended up several hundred yards away from the boat. With Mikey backing down at full speed, Will got the leader as the fish recovered from its exertions, and Clay tagged it with an underwater jab.

This sent the marlin off on another burst of jumps right behind the boat, in an impressive display that reminded us of the power of these magnificent fish. The marlin came to a halt 100 yards away, and Will got the leader a second time as Mikey brought us back to the fish. The marlin rolled on her side at the surface, and we got a clear view of the of the great fish's depth. She righted herself and swam off, forcing Will to release the leader. I cautioned him not to pull hard on the fish because I wanted to get in and film this magnificent creature before we released her, and *Chunda* was nowhere in sight.

A few minutes later, Will grabbed the leader for a third time and held too tightly — the mono parted! We decided that having spent a total of 40 minutes trolling and three hours fighting marlin, we had better call it quits and head in. Mike Latham filled out the tag cards, writing "1,000 pounds plus" in the space for estimated weight. I'd enjoyed a superb day's fishing with an excellent crew, and felt extremely lucky to have caught and released two blues in the 1,000-pound range in a single afternoon.

While on the water August 1, Peter B. Wright called us over to *Duyfken*. He'd hooked a small fish of 400 pounds to which Heidi, Barbara Block's research assistant, was going to attach a pop-up satellite tag. Peter did a great job of leading the tagged marlin past us several times, allowing us to get good footage as well as still shots of the healthy marlin. C.P. snorkeled above us and also took photos of the first blue marlin to be filmed underwater bearing a pop-up satellite tag.

Another day, I took advantage of my first chance to film a spearfish underwater. Caught on the charter boat *Cabo S João*, the colorful little fish (about 25 pounds) wore branching vertical stripes similar to a wahoo's. Spearfish bear great resemblance to white marlin in the eastern North Atlantic, with wide, rounded dorsal and anal fins. The only distinguishing feature in spearfish is the position of the anus, located about 8 to 12 inches anterior of the anal fin. In all other billfish, the anus lies immediately anterior of the anal fin.

On several occasions, we tried to get in the water with sperm whales, but they acted shy and uncooperative. Frank and Buffy Zino, residents of Funchal and good friends of Stewart and Nikki's, invited us to dinner one evening. Frank showed videos from the 1960s of the whaling operation in Madeira. Small boats would launch and paddle out to intercept passing whales spotted from the cliffs. Whalers harpooned their quarry by hand and held on for a Nantucket sleigh ride. And people think I'm crazy to dive with marlin?

The awesome videos were shot in an open boat, in color, on a small wind-up, spring-loaded 6mm camera. The whaling station is now closed, and male sperm whales cruise the coastline unmolested (save for a couple of crazy divers). João Borges had converted one of the old whaling boats to a fishing boat for the Zinos, in which they regularly troll for tuna and marlin.

The fishing remained slow, with one or two bites per day for the fleet, up to our last day on August 5. Stewart released a 60-pound white marlin on 8-pound test, providing me with some good jump shots. We trolled westward, and finally a blue came up on the left short teaser. Stewart hooked the 500-pound fish on 80-pound-test and had the fish to the boat in short order. When the fish jumped, we noticed something missing. It had no bill, just a small knob at the end of the upper jaw. Kent and I dived on the marlin, and disaster struck as my Nikonos RS flooded. I did, however, shoot some good footage of the marlin with the video camera. Twice this fish regurgitated its stomach and swallowed it, and I was able to capture the phenomenon on film. That blue was the only one *Chunda* tallied for the season.

Thanks to the anglers' and scientists' efforts, three marlin left Madeiran waters carrying pop-up tags. Each fish went in a different direction: Three months later, one tag came up halfway across the Atlantic, the second surfaced off Sierra Leone and the third off the Canaries.

I did not return to Madeira in 1998 but chose instead to visit the Cape Verde Islands in May and the Azores in September in my continued quest to film free-swimming blue marlin. The *Chunda* team did not catch a single marlin during the 1998 season in Madeira, and many boats ended up catching only one or two. While some anglers attributed the poor fishing to a lack of bait, others blamed longliners. The recreational impact on this fishery also was initially severe; local charter captains, as well as visiting crews, had weighed many large marlin in 1993 and 1994, setting all sorts of grander catch records.

The question of why oversized female marlin make up the predominant catches around Madeira remains unanswered. Females outnumber males by a ratio of 6-to-1, if you consider sport-fishing boats an unbiased sampling tool. The only two blue marlin I dissected in Madeira were females, both with inactive gonads. If the females had been in breeding condition, I would have expected to see four or more males to each female. So why do these females frequent Madeira in summer, the spawning period for the majority of North Atlantic blue marlin? The answer may lie in food availability. Large individuals of a species tend to migrate to the extremes of their ranges (in this case, water temperature represents a limiting factor) to take advantage of excellent feeding opportunities.

Fishing in Madeira has been inconsistent for the past three seasons. Are we seeing a low in biological cycles of abundance because of fluctuating oceanic conditions, or have these great fish become as scarce as certain scientists believe? According to the July 2000 ICCAT Billfish Workshop Report SCRS00/23, commercial landings of Atlantic blue marlin totaled 3,316 metric tons, while recreational anglers landed 44 metric tons, or 1.32 percent of total mortality. At present levels of longline activity (by far the greatest cause of blue marlin mortality), scientists predict blue marlin will become commercially extinct within seven years.

Billfish cannot be kept in captivity — let alone be induced to spawn — as has been achieved with tuna, dolphin and sharks. Our efforts to save blue marlin and other billfish species hinge on the reduction of fishing effort with closed areas and closed seasons in known spawning areas. Recreational user groups adhere to self-imposed catch restrictions, resulting in the release of more than 90 percent of all marlin caught in the Caribbean, Central America and the United States. Has the time come to release *all* marlin, particularly large females that form the brood stock?

Above: Blue Rampage, *acrylic on canvas.*

Opposite: A missing bill didn't hinder the feeding ability of this 500-pound blue.

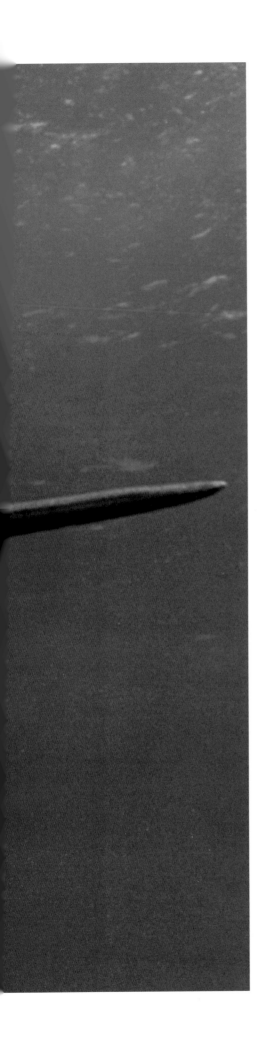

CHAPTER 9

Left: A 400-pound blue swings close to the camera for a classic head-on shot.

Below: A lighthouse is perched high above the water on the cliffs of São Pedro, São Vicento.

CAPE VERDE ISLANDS
High Winds and Cooperative Blues

The Cape Verde Islands form an archipelago about 200 miles off the coast of Dakar, Senegal, in West Africa. The islands, formerly owned and governed by the Portuguese (independent since 1975), rely heavily on tourism, with several resorts touting scuba diving as a main attraction.

I decided to visit the Cape Verde Islands in 1998 after hearing about the previous fishing season. Capt. Trevor Cockle on the *Hooker* had set world records for the most blue marlin caught in a day. In mid-May, the *Hooker* team tagged and released 15 blues in one day, only to outdo themselves a couple of days later by catching 20. This exceptional fishing represented twice the number of blues released by one boat during the best-ever day off St. Thomas, USVI! While estimating the majority at about 250 pounds, *Hooker* reported several Cape Verde fish in the 500- to 700-pound range.

Before that, in 1992, Stewart Campbell fished in Cape Verde with Barkey Garnsey and Charles "C.P." Perry on a chartered 31-foot Bertram. Besides catching several large blues on that trip, they saw what they considered to be their largest marlin to date, estimated at 1,500-plus pounds.

The intrepid explorers who joined me on this trip included Bill Boyce (my No. 2 underwater cameraman), Mikey Latham (dedicated topside cameraman) and Charlie Forman as designated angler. We left New York on a South African

Airlines jumbo headed to Johannesburg and disembarked when the plane made a refueling stop at Sal in the Cape Verde Islands. Arriving there at 3 a.m., we faced the task of salvaging our luggage amid a crowd of 300 other passengers, all Cape Verde islanders carrying six bags each. We had a six-hour layover until catching our commuter flight to Mindelo, on the island of São Vicente at the western side of the archipelago.

The island of Sal lies flat, arid and unattractive, compared with São Vicente and neighboring islands, which are steep, rugged and craggy but also arid. And the wind howls! At this time of year, northeast trades hum at 25 to 30 knots; around the edges of the islands the wind may increase to 60 knots for short periods.

Upon our arrival, we discovered the fishing had been slow with only a couple of bites per day, and green, cold water prevailed in the fishing area off São Pedro. Here, the island shelf juts out into the Atlantic, generating upwellings that bring nutrients to plankton. In the right conditions, Atlantic mackerel, bonito and yellowfin tuna congregate, attracting marlin in droves.

São Vicente sits approximately 17 degrees north of the equator, yet mackerel abound in the cool, 73-degree water. In Jamaica, at the same latitude but on the other side of the Atlantic, the water runs 10 degrees warmer than in Cape Verde. Trade winds blowing off the continental margin of West Africa push surface waters offshore, allowing cooler water to rise from the depths. The chilly, nutrient-rich waters stimulate primary productivity, resulting in an abundance of baitfish and their predators — just as occurs off the Pacific coast of Central and South America.

We decided to catch the first blue marlin raised in the teasers, as I wanted to film a good blue marlin release sequence from underwater. Mates Randy Baker and Ronnie Fields had Spanish mackerel ready to pitch on 80-pound outfits, with a 30-pound outfit set for sails or spearfish. We trolled away from São Vicente in rough seas, out toward Ilha de Santa Luzia. Huge schools of small flying fish skimmed the waves; I had never seen so many flyers get up in front of a boat in such thick clouds. However, flying fish don't always indicate the presence of blue marlin. In fact, having cut open the stomachs of more than 2,000 blue marlin in the Caribbean at different tournaments and weigh stations, I have yet to find one containing flying fish.

A hungry blue smacked the short right teaser at 1 p.m. Charlie did the honors and fought the fish for 25 minutes before Ronnie got the leader. The 400-pound marlin put on a great show. I took a lot of boat-side jump shots, then Bill and I got geared up and jumped in. Oh, the water was cold!

The frisky marlin didn't want us to get near, but as it tired out I began to close in for some great footage. On one pass I came within a couple of feet of its left side, panning down the body then swimming behind the marlin's beating tail for as long as possible to hold the shot. This particular fish displayed a huge, healed wound around the peduncle, and the second anal fin was ripped off. The wound was perhaps three or four weeks old, had healed well and in no way affected the marlin's ability to swim and feed. The fish had given a great performance on the line.

The marlin had apparently been attacked by a large predator, probably a sizable mako shark. Makos often attack from underneath and go for the peduncle, trying to immobilize a marlin or swordfish by cutting off the tail. The shark then turns to feast on its helpless victim. This blue marlin was fortunate to have escaped with only deep scars as a souvenir of the close encounter. Tagged and released by the *Hooker* team, the marlin shot away from the boat, gliding right past Bill and me on its way to freedom.

Survival, *mixed media.*
When the yellowfin tuna showed up, so did the
predators — the mako and big blue marlin.

I have seen a number of Atlantic blue marlin showing signs of recovery from massive injuries. A 305-pound blue landed in a Cayman Islands tournament had a 21-inch-wide, 10-inch-deep shark bite in the left flank above the anal fin. The gaping wound was healing over, so it obviously had occurred some time prior to the fish's capture. The attacker had to have been a large shark, probably a tiger, given the size and severity of the wound. I have seen many blues missing bills or fins without any apparent long-term negative effects.

A 120-pound blue landed in Port Antonio, Jamaica, had survived one of the worst injuries I've seen on a billfish. The first gill arch on the right side was broken, and the exposed ends had healed over completely. The marlin had probably been hooked, quite some time earlier, in such a way that it broke the gill arch. Arterial blood coming straight from the heart would have gushed out of the injury. Nonetheless, the marlin's damage control systems managed to close off the ruptured artery and heal the gill.

In many documented instances, large blue marlin have consumed other billfish such as sailfish, white marlin or spearfish. In some cases a big blue ends up with a bill or two stuck in its head or body, but the predator apparently suffers no long-term debilitation from the injury.

My point is that released marlin, even those bleeding profusely from a hook-related injury, possess remarkable powers of recovery and can survive the trauma. We find proof of this in the recapture of healthy marlin and other billfish, having been released in "poor condition" according to information on tag cards.

Back to Cape Verde: We raised a spearfish on the run home, but I missed the hookup. With nothing happening at São Pedro, Trevor decided to head for Banco Noroeste the next day, entailing a two-hour run from Mindelo across the channel to Santo Antão. In the lee of Santo Antão we got a brief respite from the nagging northeast wind, but once past the northern tip of the island we took the wind on the chin. With no spray curtains on the bridge, Trevor climbed higher to drive from the tower. Talk about getting slammed around! He's a braver man than I.

We began to troll teasers about 4 miles from the bank. I sat on the left side as usual; Bill was on the right, ready to go with cameras in hand. Ronnie and Randy had a bait box full of bonito belly strips, whole bonito, skipjacks and small yellowfin tuna to tease blues once we raised them in the spread of lures. A couple of live bonitos even swam in the baitwell. We were ready.

As we approached the bank, birds became more numerous, and curtains of flying fish unrolled around us. A blue marlin of 250 pounds popped up on the long right teaser, but faded after a half-hearted attempt at eating the lure. Yellowfin tuna hammered schools of flying fish swept up over the bank by the current, and swarming wahoo began their daylong attack on the Softhead teasers. (We'd go through a dozen teasers a day.) A blue came up on the left short — my side. I dropped in and had a great angle on a 300-pound blue that hung around for a short time. Her body was completely black, almost like a Pacific sailfish's: no stripes, no blue tail — just a black missile. She didn't participate in the teasing process, and as I followed her away, up-sea, she returned to her normal, pastel-blue cruising colors. Bill and I were now far from the boat, which was pushed by the wind and the waves, and we had to swim hard to get back. Nearing the boat, I saw another, smaller marlin at the transom, eating a live bonito. Randy had bridled the bait to a short length of 80-pound line and tied it to a fender, so the bonito zipped around in crazy circles before the marlin grabbed it.

The tension from the floating fender yanked the bonito away from the marlin; the marlin spun and grabbed the hapless baitfish again, stopped, crushed the head

Above: Bill Boyce and Harvey ready for action aboard the Hooker.

Opposite: The author chases a blue marlin to capture film for a billfish documentary. Photo by Bill Boyce.

Below: Randy Baker's bait box on the Hooker contained an array of teasers to use on the area's blue marlin.

Above: Charlie Forman hoists his 70-pound wahoo caught on Banco Noroeste.

Opposite: Blue Marlin on Yellowfin, mixed media.

and swallowed the bonito in a couple of seconds. The 80-pound line connecting the bonito to the fender broke as the marlin accelerated to chase another teaser.

A most cooperative marlin, this fellow remained jet black in its "feeding suit." It repeatedly attacked the strips and even a Mold Craft fender teaser painted to represent a skipjack tuna. Frank Johnson was pleased to see this footage! The blue stayed around for a few minutes before cruising off down-sea to look for something else to eat.

Back in the boat I was elated that Bill and I had been able to film the blue marlin doubleheader. In addition, Mikey Latham had shot decent footage, using a pole camera off the transom.

Conditions improved as we continued trolling around the bank. We caught a couple of wahoo for fun, as well as a 20-pound yellowfin tuna that was added to Randy's teaser arsenal. Since I wanted to film a blue eating a large bait, Randy rigged the fresh dead tuna on an 80-pound outfit.

In the afternoon a hot 300-pounder came charging on the long right teaser. It crossed over to the left, and as Ronnie reeled it closer, I went in and got some great close-up footage before the marlin became disinterested and turned away suddenly. Bill and I trailed the fish as it headed away in no great hurry. Trevor, seeing what was happening from the bridge, took the initiative and gunned the *Hooker* around in front of the departing marlin. As the boat moved ahead, Ronnie fired out the 20-pound yellowfin and kept it skipping in the wake next to a teaser.

Galvanized into action by the change in motion, the marlin grabbed the lure before spinning around and taking the tuna crosswise in its pointed jaws. Bill and I swam as hard as possible to get into position, and we both nailed the sequence. Having got the tuna, the marlin stopped swimming but turned away from us. It shuffled the tuna around so the head pointed down its gullet. The stripes on the marlin's back turned on and stood out vividly against the black background. The marlin flared its gills and sucked in the tuna, then swam off with the yellowfin's tail sticking out of its mouth.

Unbelievable! The whole process took five seconds.

Back at the boat, Ronnie was still tight to the marlin, which was pulling 28 pounds of drag off the 80-pound rig. He had tried to pull the tuna away from the marlin, but without success. The marlin swallowed the tuna in spite of pressure from Ronnie, which made the proceedings even more amazing. When a hungry marlin sets its mind on eating, little will deter it. Within minutes the 80-pound mono chaffed against the marlin's jaw, and Ronnie reeled in a slack line.

The next day, April 25, we returned to the washing machine at Banco Noroeste with winds shrieking at about 35 knots. Shearwaters and petrels were active, as were tuna and wahoo. Three commercial boats were live-baiting for tuna, and several pangas trolled for wahoo. We raised no marlin, which proved disappointing after having seen five the previous day.

On April 26, I awoke to find the crew alert and standing ready. Winds cranked at 60 knots in the harbor, and a couple of vessels passed us, dragging anchors. Several old wrecks littered the harbor's shoreline, and we could easily see — with conditions like this — that grounding represented a regular hazard.

By 10:30, the wind calmed completely. We went trolling in the channel between São Vicente and Santo Antão, raising a blue marlin at noon on the left short teaser. The fish was very close when I jumped in, and I obtained good footage of it charging the teaser. This fish must have been on amphetamines, spinning around and charging upward as if it hadn't eaten for days, demonstrating remarkable

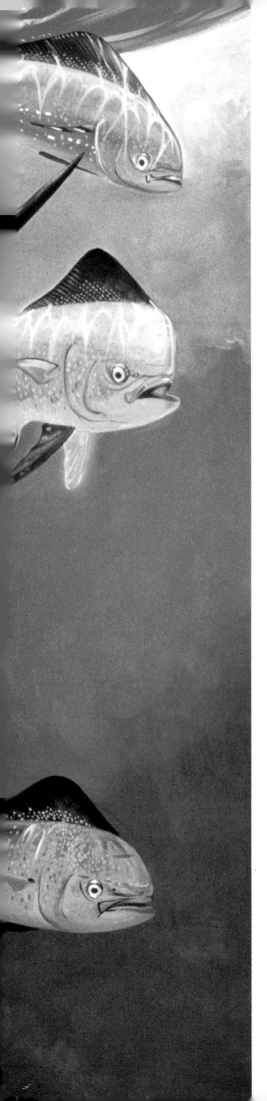

Opposite: Blue and Green, *acrylic on canvas.*

Below: Ronnie Fields wires one of Charlie's
most active blue marlin.

speed and maneuverability. This was the fastest I had seen a marlin swim. The frantic fish provided great entertainment for 4 ½ minutes before fading off.

We returned to São Pedro but still raised no marlin in the spot where they normally concentrate. The crew persisted until 6 p.m. and enjoyed a smooth ride home for a change.

Morning dawned calm in the harbor on April 27, so after catching live bait at São Pedro and trolling for an hour, we decided to run back to Banco Noroeste. But as we reached Santo Antão, the wind came blowing like a hammer out of the north. We hadn't felt its effect in Mindelo, which lies in the lee of Santo Antão. Trolling in the channel south of Santo Antão for the rest of the day failed to produce so much as a nibble.

I knew April 28 was going to be a tough day when we awoke to 35-knot winds in the harbor. We trolled at São Pedro for a while, where conditions remained at least moderate, then turned southeast toward Ilheu Branco. Five miles out, we ran smack into a wind acceleration zone that gave us a good scare. Tremendous winds tore off the wave tops and whipped white foam into the air while small twisters careened all around us, howling through the riggers and halyards. Trevor performed an immediate about-face and got us out of there pronto.

We trolled back past Santo Antão and into the channel, where the wind eased and then dropped out. The water became blue and warm; we soon spotted birds and a school of shy pilot whales. Bill and I swam with them for a few minutes, but the big bull herded the school away from us.

We continued pulling teasers, and at 3 p.m. a 400-pound blue marlin came up on the long right teaser but soon faded off. Trevor put the *Hooker* in a tight turn, running around the fish on the surface. She reappeared behind the long left and teased in really well — on my side of the cockpit again. When I jumped in, I landed on her head. Startled, she kicked away all striped up, then spun around and attacked the Softhead/belly-strip teaser with immense speed and force. She stopped each time and chewed the teaser before Randy snatched it away. The fish proved very cooperative, staying jet black and swimming close to Bill and me for excellent photo opportunities.

The mates sent out a live 5-pound bonito, and the marlin raced in to grab it. Ronnie pulled it away — perhaps prematurely, as I was in great position to film the blue swallowing the bonito. The persistent marlin took the bonito again and swallowed it this time, but, unfortunately, while facing away from me. Feeling pressure from the line, the blue shook its head a couple of times and then swam straight back up into the pattern to start feeding again. It stayed around the boat for a little while longer, displaying an array of color changes and aggressive feeding behavior before heading off.

The weather became worse and worse as we trolled back toward São Pedro and on to Mindelo. We passed through another dangerous zone of incredible wind speed and crawled home at about 5 knots. Trevor admitted for the first time that he felt "a little concerned" about sea conditions and the force of the wind.

On our seventh day, April 29, we decided to check out São Pedro before making the two-hour run to Banco Noroeste. The wind remained moderate, but swells ran huge. As usual, we saw plenty of birds and thick rafts of flying fish. The first blue came up at 11:50 a.m. on the short left. The 500-pounder ate the strip bait three times, stopping to chew it before Randy yanked it away. Each time the marlin would sink to 30 feet and attack from underneath.

When the fish neared the surface, Ronnie sent out a 15-pound yellowfin tuna that the marlin promptly grabbed — immediately above me — before turning and dropping it. The marlin spun around and eyed the sinking tuna with caution. Ronnie retrieved and cast again. The marlin sauntered up and took the tuna, but dropped it once more. It would look at the strip baits repeatedly, but without eating. The marlin had gone totally black when attacking the baits, but while circling it turned a magnificent dark blue with bronze flanks and purple tail. Charlie had joined us on this fish and captured some great still shots.

Peter B. Wright and his crew had been making their way south from the Canaries on the *Duyfken* with a motor sailboat for a mothership. They went through the same foul weather we experienced, but arrived safely, albeit battered. They visited the *Madam* and over a couple of drinks told the story of their eventful trip. I showed Peter some of the footage we'd taken throughout the week. Impressed, he remarked how the videos could help anglers. Seeing how quickly blue marlin can swallow a bait would help refine angling techniques.

In nine days, we'd raised 20 blues, dived on 14 and caught one, and had put together the most comprehensive footage to date on free-swimming blue marlin. I couldn't help feeling, however, that we might have seen just as many marlin in St. Thomas or Venezuela.

On the other hand, we ended up victims of a frustrating case of "you should have stayed a couple more days." Two days after we departed São Vicente, the next charter arrived and Trevor fished them a half-day at São Pedro. Those anglers released 12 marlin the first afternoon and tallied 50 more in the following five days!

Below: Blue Surprise, *acrylic on canvas.*

*Below: A series of video frames shows
a blue marlin swimming away
moments after its release.*

Above: Whites on Mackerel, *mixed media.*

*Opposite: A 3,000-foot caldera looms in
the distance behind Castelo Branco on
Faial's south side.*

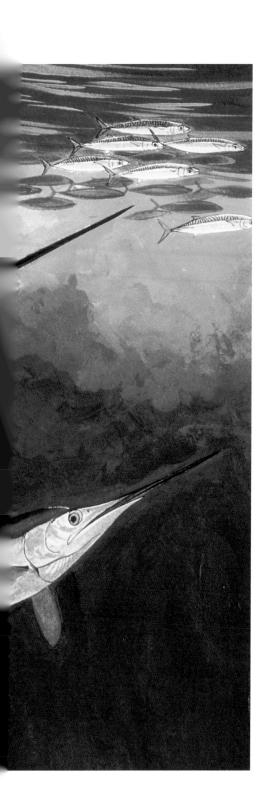

CHAPTER 10

THE AZORES
White Marlin Save the Day

The Mid-Atlantic Ridge runs north to south for several thousand miles along the floor of the Atlantic Ocean. This geologic structure features a group of volcanic mountains whose tips rise above the sea approximately 800 miles west of Portugal to form the Azorean archipelago. The Azores include nine islands and seven small islets, plus a number of seamounts which do not reach the surface.

The area remains volcanically active and of great interest to geologists and tourists. On July 9, 1998 — just two months before my visit — a serious earthquake shook the island of Faial with an intensity of 8 on the Mercali scale, killing eight people and destroying more than a thousand homes. Faial itself consists of a tremendous cinder cone now covered in forest, with a mile-wide caldera crowning the island and a line of vents stretching to the west. In 1957 a massive eruption added several square miles to the island seaward of the historic lighthouse.

Discovered in 1432 by the Portuguese, the Azores, like Madeira, remain a Portuguese island state. An important stop for shipping, their strategic location also makes them an ideal base for military operations. Commercial fishing and whaling have been replaced with whale-watching and tourism as the mainstays for local business.

Though located between 37 and 40 degrees north, the Azores are washed by an eastward flowing branch of the Gulf Stream called the Azores Current. Fluctuations in this current greatly influence the availability of baitfish and their predators. When we arrived on September 1, 1998, the fishing had been slow. Jerry and Deborah Dunaway had caught just two blue marlin and one giant bluefin tuna in 20 days of fishing on the *Hooker*. While my aim was to film big blue marlin and tuna, we could always switch our emphasis to the more abundant white marlin if necessary.

The *Madam* was anchored in the main port in Horta, the capital of Faial. Across the channel loomed the island of Pico, with its splendid 7,000-foot volcanic peak. Every morning Pico wore a different face that changed with the cloud cover. Recalling the view of Pico from Horta, I can think of no more beautiful spot to begin and end a day's fishing.

*Above: A white marlin grabs a live mackerel
at the surface.*

*Opposite: Another white grabs a live mackerel,
dives and drags a bubble trail
deep into the blue.*

Thousands of ship and yacht emblems painted on the flagstones and seawalls deco-rate Horta's large, well-maintained harbor. A small fleet of famous marlin boats and their captains work here. Some of the best known names include Capt. Jo Franck of *Double Header*, Capt. Didier Armand and Capt. Don Merten, now on the new *Capri*, and boats such as *Shanghai, Xacara* and *Cepheus*, to name a few.

Jo Franck's wife, Greet Wouters, wrote and published a marvelous book about the his-tory of fishing in the Azores: *Close to the Surface*. This collector's item stands out as an authoritative commentary on the birth of sport fishing in the region and documents the exploitation of marine resources that once were abundant around the archipelago.

Our team consisted of the usual gang: Bill Boyce, Mikey Latham and Charlie Forman, plus Kaye Pearson and my friend from Jamaica, Donna Robinson. An accomplished angler, Donna caught a grander blue marlin the previous season on her boat, *Can't Touch Dis*, in Madeira. She also holds the distinction of catching four blue marlin in one day — twice — in Port Antonio, Jamaica, and is the only female angler to have accom-plished this.

It was blowing hard the day we arrived, but winds calmed for our first day of fishing, September 2. A large ground swell persisted as we headed out to the Azores Bank, 22 miles south of Faial, and trolled with hooks for a couple of hours. Trevor then picked up and ran another 20 miles offshore to Princess Alice Bank, which features a high spot that comes within 120 feet of the surface — very diveable! Birds worked the area, and we caught a wahoo for dinner before switching to teasers. Charlie and Donna each

caught a white marlin on pitch baits, and we put those fish to good use. Bill and I jumped in and filmed the small marlin, shooting the releases underwater. The remarkably clear water on the bank offered about 200 feet of horizontal visibility. As we filmed the hooked whites, other free-swimming white marlin passed close by. We also filmed a huge school of skipjacks with a few small yellowfin tuna mixed in.

During the two-hour run home, we heard that the other boats had raised four marlin on Condor Bank, to the west of Faial. Perhaps we'd try there tomorrow.

September 3 started out windy, but the breeze died as we got to Condor Bank. Some other boats were trolling there as well. We caught only one white marlin, while *Shangai* fought a big blue for 2 ½ hours before losing it. Many white marlin had been seen on the Azores Bank, so our plan for tomorrow was to tease and film whites underwater all day and get some action footage in the can.

Observing great numbers of birds, porpoises and skipjack tuna on the Azores Bank made September 4 as pleasant a day as it gets on the ocean. However, we didn't raise a billfish until 2 p.m. — but then they came in threes and tens! Bill and I shot some great action sequences of the cooperative white marlin, partly because we switched to using live mackerel and *chicharro* (a type of jack mackerel). The whites didn't hesitate to take these baitfish, often swimming right past us to chase and catch their prey.

White marlin look like smaller versions of striped marlin, exhibiting beautiful colors and broad, rounded fins. Twisting and turning in pursuit of baitfish, their backs reflect the light in metallic sheens of black, blue and purple, with bronze flanks banded by vivid, fluorescent-blue stripes. When the fish get very excited, the stripes become so bright they look white. Usually the pectoral and tail fins glow fluorescent powder blue against the dark background of the deep-blue ocean. Close up, we noticed subtle metallic pinks and emerald and bronze highlights on their faces and opercula.

One white marlin hung around for 25 minutes, eating a dozen mackerel in the process. The mates, Ronnie and Randy, did a superb job of teasing this marlin while Mikey filmed the action topside. Once, the white caught a live mackerel right in front of me and dove about 20 feet, stopped to crush the head and turned the bait to swallow it headfirst in a flash. It was unusual to see a billfish swallow with head angled down and tail up, as the majority I've seen do it the other way around, with head up. In nature there are no hard and fast rules when it's time to eat.

Some of the whites would catch a live mackerel and swim some distance away from the others, then crush the bait's head before swallowing it. Then they rejoined the group of marlin waiting to feed. Randy would throw in a handful of mackerel, which headed for the horizon only to be picked off by the marlin. Occasionally a mackerel would go straight down and temporarily avoid the voracious marlin, but inevitably a white would race downward and catch the bait far below, almost out of sight. I could see this because the bait always flashed silvery in a marlin's mouth, seconds before being swallowed. The white would then swim vertically up at me and rejoin the action. The rising marlin was hard to spot against the indigo water, and the only thing that gave it away was a silvery patch in the throat region clearly visible from ahead of the fish. If I had been a baitfish swimming merrily along at the surface, I would never have seen this swift predator rocketing up at me from the depths until it was too late.

L ater in the afternoon we found a large school of skipjack tuna under birds. Bill and I dived and filmed for half an hour, hoping to get lucky and see a predator with them. As the *Hooker* moved slowly around us, the skipjacks rose in a cloud to investigate the foamy wake, seeking small baitfish. I've witnessed this interesting behavioral response of skipjack and yellowfin tuna many times in other locations. A foamy boat wake — even without a spread of lures — mimics feeding activity and attracts tuna. Would the same apply for billfish?

Below: A local tuna boat leaves Horta to fish the Princess Alice Bank.

Above: Randy Baker and Ronnie Fields show off a white marlin caught on a spinning-rod teaser (no hook).

Opposite: Teased White*, mixed media. Harvey considers the pink-and-white Softhead with bonito belly strip his best teaser combination.*

*Above: Harvey captured this classic portrait of a
white marlin switching its attention from the
teaser to a live mackerel.*

*Opposite: Ronnie Fields, Harvey and Bill Boyce
end a successful white marlin shoot.*

We finished up the day diving on a couple more teased white marlin, making a total of 20 for the day on camera. I felt a lot better now that we had some great underwater action on film. That evening after dinner, we were treated to a tour of the town's whaling and scrimshaw museum. It is the largest collection of scrimshaw art I have ever seen, containing hundreds of sperm-whale teeth and whalebone items, beautifully worked and etched, with subject matter ranging from sailing and whaling scenes to nudes. We stayed up late and consequently had a slow start the following day, which turned out windy and rough. Fishing around the eastern side of Faial, in a spot called Riberinha, kept us somewhat in the lee. In the afternoon we saw hundreds of birds wheeling over schools of common dolphin feeding on mackerel, but we raised no marlin or tuna.

On September 6 we headed back to the Azores Bank, seeking more white marlin footage. Our first bite proved spectacular as we raised a group of seven fish. Bill and I filmed excellent teasing sequences; one 80-pound white marlin was particularly cooperative. Later that morning we filmed an 8-foot smooth hammerhead as he hovered around a group of petrels fighting over a mackerel carcass. Although we raised no blues that day, another boat caught and released a 700-pounder on the same bank.

With little action at Condor or Azores banks, we returned to Princess Alice Bank on September 7. White marlin rose to our teasers in groups of five or more. After filming all morning, we decided to dive on the bank's high spot. Bill, Randy and I descended to the top of the pinnacle in 120 feet. The cold water remained clear in spite of some freshwater upwelling. The bare rock structure held a wide variety of fish life, including schools of healthy-looking almaco jacks, chevron barracudas and triggerfish that escorted us as we looked around. A school of manta rays swam over us, high in the water column, and we rose to meet them and capture the scene on film. As we neared the surface, schools of yellowfin tuna and Atlantic bonito zoomed overhead while wahoo lurked in the distance. The wonderful dive would be worth repeating, should conditions allow.

We resumed trolling, now with hooked lures, and encountered our first blue marlin. It sneaked in on the left short, and Donna caught the fish smartly in 15 minutes. The

250-pounder refused to jump until she brought it close to the boat. We tagged it, took a few photographs and released the fish, finally breaking our run of poor luck on blues.

On September 8, we returned to Princess Alice Bank and found two commercial tuna boats fishing over the high spot. They were spraying and jack-poling skipjack and yellowfin to 30 pounds. We filmed this fishing procedure topside, then Bill and I slid over the side to get underwater sequences. A mass of fish swarmed beneath the tuna boat. Purse seines would have wiped them out, but these guys caught them the old-fashioned way — they used directed and selective harvest without overexploiting the resource.

We dropped our marker on the high spot, close to the drifting tuna boats. Trevor, Bill and I dived while Trevor tried to salvage a Bruce anchor on the bottom. I concentrated on filming the variety of small grouper, triggerfish and beautifully marked moray eels on the bottom. While all this was going on down below, a group of seven manta rays swam by the *Hooker* at the surface. Unable to resist, all hands jumped in and snorkeled with them. There is nothing like a good dive to add variety and adventure to a day of trolling.

Once we resumed trolling, we filmed five pods of white marlin and hooked another six whites to get more catch-and-release action footage. One fish's bill had broken off, and the site had healed over completely. This specimen added variety to our collection of images. I couldn't help but wonder what close encounter caused this marlin to lose its bill.

Rather than going back to Princess Alice Bank, as we probably should have, we fished off Riberinha and around the north side of Faial to Condor Bank on September 9. Trolling close to shore, we enjoyed spectacular views of the island rising in a forested cinder cone to the cloud-covered caldera. In contrast, the stark western side looks like a moonscape where no vegetation has grown since the last volcanic eruption. On the way in, we paused for photos at Castelo Branco, a dramatic product of volcanic activity that created a buttress of rock projecting into the sea.

The next day at Princess Alice Bank brought spectacular action. The whites were plentiful, and every school contained four or more fish. We prepared for them by loading the baitwell full of mackerel and *chicharro*. In the middle of all this jumping in and out and filming, a 500-pound blue marlin crashed the right long teaser. Kaye Pearson was up. He sent out a mackerel and hooked up. The marlin put on a great show and after 40 minutes, Kaye notched his personal best while Bill and I jumped into the water to film the release. The marlin was cleanly hooked in the lower jaw; Randy removed the hook, then turned the fish upright. As the blue paddled off slowly, I raced along its right side, camera rolling, swimming at full speed to stay in position next to its face. It turned out to be a good close-up shot, and as I ran out of air I let the fish swim away to be absorbed by the indigo blue.

We ended up filming many more white marlin, as they provide a great deal of action as well as good fun. I spent the whole afternoon shooting still shots of the whites, one of which had a left pectoral fin missing.

Our last day was equally action-packed. A tuna boat fished the high spot on Princess Alice Bank while we trolled around and raised pods of white marlin. Randy even caught one on a spinning rod, with just a teaser and no hook! The fish wrapped the short leader on its bill and couldn't shake loose. The furious white went ballistic, and we divers kept our heads down and out of the charging fish's way. Strangely, other nearby marlin continued circling and feeding, seemingly unconcerned with the noisy struggle. Not to be outdone, Charlie hooked and released his first white marlin on fly while Bill and I were in the water — another dramatic display of acrobatic leaps of which we shot the underwater half of the action.

Sword Daze, *mixed media. The waters around
the Azores are loaded with yellowfin and bigeye
tuna, which attract big predators such as
broadbill swordfish.*

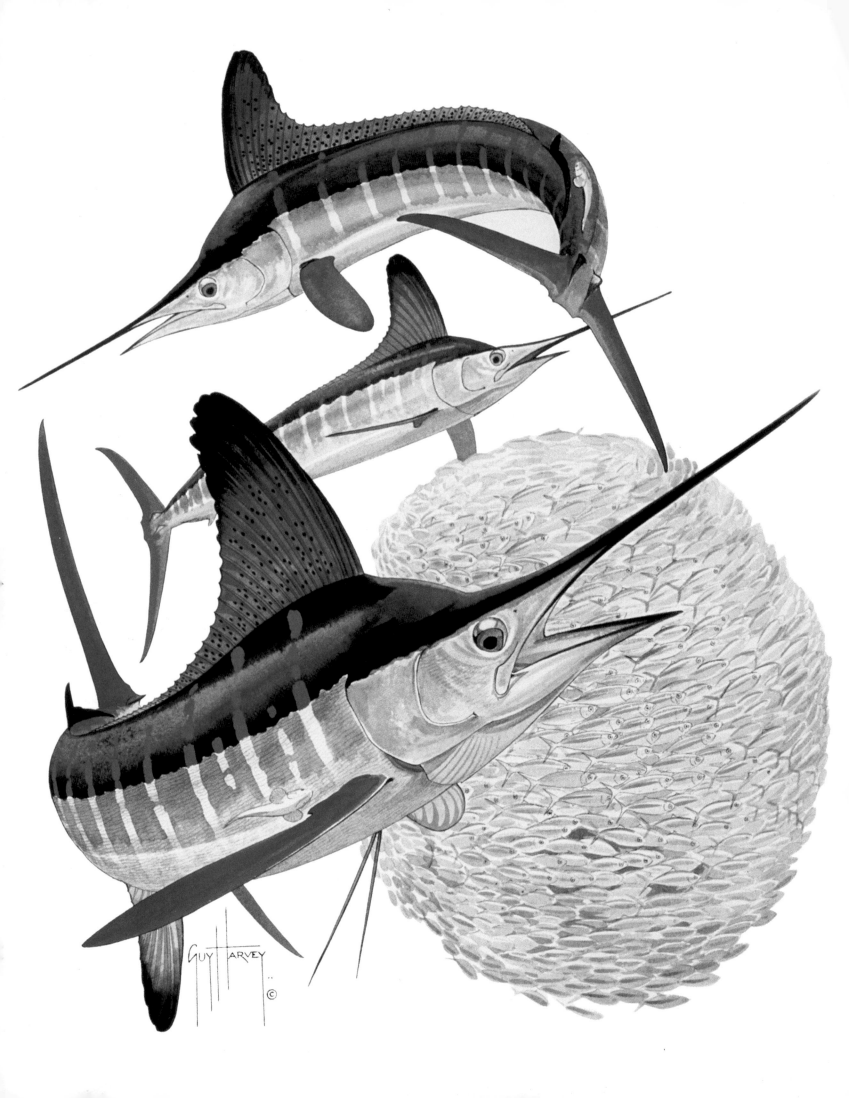

Working around the tuna boat, we could see the massive, dark shape of the skipjack school below, but the fishermen were not catching many. When Bill and I went in to get shots, the school stayed skittish — even when we unloaded a bucket of small *chicharro* into their midst. Something was alarming them. Trevor went alongside the tuna boat and spoke to the captain, who said a marlin was terrorizing the school of tuna. It was unlikely that we'd tease the marlin up unless we used live skipjacks.

Ronnie and I each put out a feather on 30-pound bait rods rigged with top shots of 80-pound leader to the hook. Within minutes, we hung two 8-pound skipjacks and were reeling them to the boat. A hungry predator does not pass up a chance like this, and we were attacked! The marlin crashed my skipjack in a flurry of spray 20 yards from the boat, then promptly turned around and ate Ronnie's skipjack in a huge boil of foam. I love seeing an oceanic predator do what it knows best! The strike happens so fast that if you blink you'll miss the show. I left my reel in free-spool. When Ronnie tried to pull his bait away from the marlin, his hook came out.

The marlin, all black with tail and pectoral fins lit up, swam up and circled around the transom. Trevor shouted to drop back a mackerel on a heavy rig, as nobody was ready to dive on the fish. I reeled up the slack on my bait rod, and, coming tight on the marlin, told Trevor that I had the fish on. Not the ideal situation: The Shimano reel held chaffed 30-pound line that had already seen a year of bait-catching duty. In addition, I only had a short leader of 80-pound-test tied to a small hook. My chances of staying attached to this 500-pound marlin for long seemed quite low.

The marlin finally woke up and took off with the *Hooker* pursuing at full speed. I backed off the drag, not wanting to stress the old line as the fish raced off, greyhounding toward Bermuda. We chased the marlin for a good 15 minutes, when suddenly the *Hooker* veered off to the left. Trevor had lost steering! He spun the boat around using only the twin engines and gears and continued to pursue the marlin in reverse — slower, but effective.

The marlin ran out of gas and slowed considerably. I finally got the 80-pound top shot on the reel and put some heat on the fish, bringing it close to the surface. The *Hooker* roared at full speed in reverse. Trying to reach the marlin, Ronnie leaned out far from the port corner of the transom, then slipped and fell in! Luckily, he was in the corner, and the big wave of the boat's backward motion pushed him around the transom and not under the stern. It was a close call.

Trevor stopped our backward charge to retrieve Ronnie, then we got back on the fish. Ronnie said with a smile that it was a decent fish, so Bill asked why he hadn't tagged the marlin while he was under there — slacker! Ronnie soon tagged the marlin's left flank with an underwater jab, which sparked the fish into another series of jumps before it sounded.

Having technically earned the release and tagged the marlin, I put the drag up to full, hoping to stop the fish or break it off. It kept going down, but finally stopped. I thumbed the reel and put great pressure on the line; the marlin started toward the surface and I got her all the way up when the 80-pound mono chaffed through, setting her free.

The exciting catch served as another remarkable learning experience. The blue marlin had eaten two 8-pound skipjacks in the space of five seconds, swallowed them both and came looking for more. And I had caught a respectable marlin on light gear, discovering the true capacity of 30-pound line while pushing it to the limit — all this with one of the world's best crews backing me up. Thank goodness, we did not lose one of them in the process.

Overall, the Azores experience had been tremendous. It was the first time I had been in the water with so many marlin, and I was beginning to identify patterns in their feeding habits that I could compare with those of other species.

Below: Bill Boyce jumps in and surprises a big white marlin, which turns to get a closer look at the new intruder.

Opposite: White Marlin and Bait Ball, *watercolor.*

Above: Giant bluefin tuna swim in the almadraba in Barbate. Bill Boyce, in the background, gives some perspective to the huge size of these tuna.

Opposite: The northern tip of Lanzarote, adjacent to the island of Graciosa.

CHAPTER 11

SOUTHERN SPAIN AND THE CANARIES
Joining the Hunt for Bluefin Tuna

A successful industrialist from the Basque country of northern Spain, José Luis Beistegui also owns several hotels in Lanzarote, in the Canary Islands. He loves to fish in his 61-foot Davis, *Karramarro III*, which translates as "Rock Crab III" — an unlikely name for such a rocket ship.

Bill Boyce and I visited José Luis to film a phenomenon that occurs each spring and summer in the channel between Lanzarote and the mainland Moroccan coast. Commercial fishermen find schools of skipjack and bigeye tuna in the spring by trolling. Once they locate a school, chumming with a steady trickle of small, live mackerel keeps tuna around the boat for extensive periods. Twice each day, in the early morning and late evening, the fishermen harvest tuna, using jackpoles. José Luis arranged for us to dive under the tuna boats and to film the proceedings over a three-day period in July 1999.

Tuna boats operating in the channel work in highly coordinated pairs; one vessel fishes while a partner boat catches bait and keeps it alive in pens until it's time to head out for several days of fishing. The boats move along at about 1 1/2 knots, and the tuna follow them, being fed from time to time. Switching on floodlights at night attracts a variety of squid and baitfish, thereby providing another source of food to help hold tuna in the vicinity. The boats stay about 5 miles apart, so their schools of tuna do not mix.

The boat captains say that big blue marlin feed on the tuna day and night. One skipper says his wooden-hulled vessel nearly sank when a marlin accidentally rammed it while chasing tuna. At times, marlin harass tuna and cause them to bunch up under the hull so densely that some get chopped by the propeller. We were hoping to film this predator/prey interaction.

Tuna refuse to feed while predators lurk nearby, so the commercial fishermen try to catch bothersome marlin, using dead skipjack tuna on a big hook and heavy leader attached to a rope. The rope is wrapped on a hydraulic winch to pull in hooked blues, which are quickly dispatched — not exactly IGFA rules. The captains tell of catching

Orca Blues, acrylic on canvas.
Life and death in the Strait of Gilbralter is seen in the orcas' relentless hunt of tuna.

800- to 1,200-pound marlin this way. In spite of their persistence, big blues do not drive a school of tuna away from the host boat, nor do sharks that occasionally appear.

The captain's worst fear is that a pack of orcas may come by and attack the tuna, which then scatter and do not return, forcing the boat to acquire fish all over again.

On July 24, we left the dock at 4 a.m. to go 20 miles offshore. José Luis arranged to rendezvous with a tuna boat, and we were told to be in position to dive under the boat at first light. We crossed over from *Karramarro III* to the tuna boat in a rubber dinghy in the dark, with José Luis driving. A huge "breezer" of skipjacks surrounded the boat while the fishermen hauled up a few bigeye. The crew used only live mackerel as bait, and they sprayed water over the side to mimic a feeding frenzy and induce tuna to bite.

Unfortunately, the light was too poor to film underwater, though I tried for a while to capture images of tuna rising to the boat to feed. So we waited for an hour, then went ahead of the tuna boat to get in the water and hang at 80 feet while it passed slowly overhead. This plan worked well, and we met the skipjacks (a school of 200-plus tons in Bill's estimation) ahead of the boat. We stayed in one spot as they poured past us, with the larger bigeye below. We repeated this procedure and thanked the captain of the boat for his cooperation. He called us over and kindly gave us an 80-pound bigeye to take home. We then made our way back to the *Karramarro III*, which waited a mile away. (Spanish maritime law mandates that a vessel may not approach closer than 1 nautical mile from a tuna boat engaged in fishing.)

We returned to Puerto Calero, cleaned up and had fresh tuna for lunch before heading to the small island of Graciosa, north of Lanzarote. Graciosa hosts a small fishing village and picturesque harbor full of colorful vessels, with the steep cliffs of Lanzarote looming in the background across the channel. Here we were fortunate to find four other tuna boats. They had already caught plenty of mackerel and held the baitfish in cylindrical pens or "keepers" beside the vessels. Bill and I took this opportunity to film bait in the keepers to document this integral part of the fishing process.

The next day José Luis made arrangements with another boat to rendezvous at 10 a.m. some 15 miles east of Graciosa. We planned to film under the boat while the crew tossed live bait and raised the tuna. This worked well; Bill and I met the school of bigeye about 300 yards ahead of the boat and 100 feet down. José Luis stayed above our bubbles in the dinghy to mark our position for the tuna-boat captain. He slowed down over us and then drifted so we did not have to swim too hard to keep up while the crew started to dole out bait. The skipjack responded immediately and provided us with a lot of good action. We had to go down 100 to 130 feet to see the bigeyes hanging deep. They came close by and gave us some good passes, but were a little shy of our bubbles (this would have been the right situation to use a rebreather). Another tuna boat began closing in from the south, so we said our thanks as the captain had to get moving again. This second dive allowed us to film in much better conditions, but we did not encounter any other fish besides tuna.

On our last day, July 26, the weather improved. Bill and I descended to 100 feet as the tuna boat slowly passed over us and stopped to drift. About 150 tons of bigeye tuna started milling around when the boat stopped, allowing me to shoot them with the hull of the boat visible at the surface. Meanwhile, feeding had begun, and the skipjacks were not shy.

After half an hour of this, José Luis got permission for us to board the tuna boat. They were going to break their morning-evening routine and catch tuna at midday for us to film. We hopped aboard still in our wetsuits. Bill took still shots while I ran around the deck with the video. The crew were delighted to help out, catching several dozen skipjacks before the shy bigeye started to bite. While boating a dozen bigeye in the 40- to 90-pound class, the fishermen released several 20-pounders in a clear demonstration that they recognize the importance of sensible fishing practices.

The whole, ungutted tuna were then washed down and packed in ice. The crew gladly showed us the hold and how they store the catch. In broken Spanish, Bill told the crew how much we appreciated their cooperation and that we were filming a documentary on billfish and tuna. When he explained that we dived with marlin and sailfish all over the world, our hosts were amazed. This led to more stories of marlin attacking tuna under the boats, with grand displays describing the size and aggression of the blues. I figured the only way to get footage of a marlin attacking tuna would require staying on a tuna boat for a full trip, ready to drop in the water when the billfish showed up for dinner.

For our next adventure, José Luis accompanied us to Malaga and introduced us to Dr. Alberto Iriarte and his wife, Maria. Alberto is a renowned heart surgeon, keen diver and fisherman who owns a fleet of three charter boats that fish for bluefin tuna out of Marbella from June through October.

Alberto had been in contact with Aniceto Ramirez, the owner of a tuna pen (*almadraba*) in Barbate. He had given Alberto permission to dive in the holding pen to film giant tuna. This seemed too good to be true, so on July 27 we drove west from Malaga, past Gibraltar and on to Zahara de los Atuns.

A metal sculpture of tuna greets motorists at the roundabout on the way to Zahara. Bluefin tuna act as the cultural symbol of this part of the Spanish coast, just as salmon

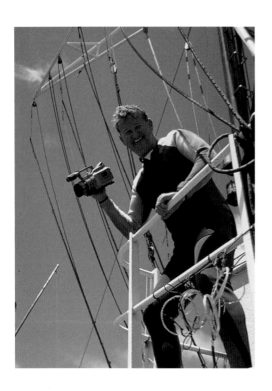

Harvey films on a tuna boat as jackpolers
catch skipjack and bigeye.
Photo by Bill Boyce.

in the Pacific Northwest, sailfish in Florida and turtles in the Cayman Islands. Local restaurants offer a variety of tuna dishes: dried, salted, in strips, chunks, cakes, dips and soup — even the ovaries, intestines and heart are considered delicacies. Nowhere was it served raw or as a rare tuna steak, as you find in the Orient or the U.S.

During dinner one evening, Alberto, Maria and José Luis explained the fascinating story of the origin of the *almadrabas* and how they rely on the migratory habits of giant bluefin tuna to catch these huge fish. The history lesson spanned more than 2,000 years of interaction and dependence on this oceanic nomad in the Mediterranean. When the species was abundant, traps set at vantage points perpendicular to the shore intercepted tuna in Turkey, Cyprus, Italy, France and Spain. Similar traps caught bluefin on the southern side of the Mediterranean in Tunisia and Morocco. The Phoenicians, Greeks and Romans all knew how to salt, pickle and preserve tuna.

The Phoenicians set up the first traps near Barbate on this part of the Spanish coast more than 2,200 years ago. The fish-salting industry and the sauces derived from fermentation of tuna innards (garum, perhaps the precursor to Viagra) constituted the main sources of the community's wealth. The abundance of bluefin led to the economic boom during the reign of the Emperor Claudius (41-54 A.D.), who conferred the rank of Roman Municipium on the town. The economic decline of Baelo Claudia began in the latter half of the second century A.D. because of an earthquake that hit the area. The town revived during the third century but was finally abandoned in the seventh century A.D. The Moors took over southern Spain in the 10th century A.D., and continued catching tuna in traps they called *almadraba*.

The name has survived, though the locals drop the "al" and simply say *madraba*. Italians call the traps *matanza*.

Maria and Alberto explained that the *almadraba* has a specific configuration to catch fish heading east when bluefin migrate into the Mediterranean from the Atlantic. These fish, in spawning condition and rich in fat, are harvested every day or every other day. Later in July, fishermen change the trap's configuration to catch the spawned fish migrating out of the Mediterranean. Because these fish are thinner and have a low fat content, they are held in a large pen (*la piscina*) and fed for three months before harvest and sale to the Japanese at an optimal price.

At the time of our arrival, 800 giant bluefin tuna occupied *la piscina*, consuming 14 tons of food per day. I was eager to swim with these great fish and get close to them for reference for future artwork. On July 28, we went to Barbate to see Aniceto Ramirez. Apparently, Alberto's request to dive in the *almadraba* had created waves: No one from the outside was allowed to dive with the tuna. A very persuasive Maria begged on our behalf, and Aniceto eventually relented. The *almadraba* captain, Vicente, and the chief diver, Luciano, eventually fell to Maria's charms as well. We got the OK: Show up at 8 o'clock sharp tomorrow morning. We were in!

I was excited, but we still had the rest of the day ahead of us. We went back to Tarifa at the southernmost point of Spain, where only 8 miles of the Strait of Gibraltar separate Spain from Morocco — a strategic place to set a tuna trap. But the *almadraba* at Tarifa had already been brought ashore, cleaned and stored by mid-July. If nothing else, though, the visit gave me a chance to appreciate the amount of hardware involved in the process. A half-acre of 2-ton anchors drove the point home quite nicely.

At this time of year, local Tarifa fishermen were engaged in fishing for tuna on lines dropped 1,500 feet to the bottom using disposable 25-pound concrete blocks for weight. A hydraulic winch lifted struggling fish to the surface to be gaffed and hauled aboard. The boats often caught two or three giant bluefin per day using this method. This practice, however, attracts the attention of orcas, the bluefin's major predator.

We waited on the commercial dock in Tarifa as local boats started to trickle in after 3 p.m. The fishermen motored up in brightly painted boats and lifted their catch to the dock by crane, then lowered the tuna onto a trolley and wheeled them inside the fish market. The babble of conversation at the dock suddenly erupted when a mutilated tuna was hoisted into view. The 600-pounder had its belly ripped off! Through José Luis, I learned an orca had attacked the bluefin. Another came up with an identical wound, and another. The next bellyless fish had its operculum torn off, exposing the gills. The fifth fish, over 700 pounds, had no belly as well as puncture marks along the gill cover. One orca had held it while another ate the belly.

Bill suggested that the orcas were targeting only the belly meat because of its high fat content. I could imagine a group of orcas waiting at the surface until the fishermen brought the tuna up from the depths and then attacking an easy target, taking the best part of the fish.

José Luis, translating a fisherman's account, said a group of more than 100 orcas was working this area of the Straits, so catches were lower today than in the past few days. I was beginning to appreciate what an effective predator of the tuna the orca had become, but like any predator it will take advantage of an easy meal. We hung around as 35 bluefins were landed, the largest weighing 761 pounds. In an auction that followed, most fish appeared to go to two buyers, for an average price of just under $3 per pound. The fish were weighed, butchered and loaded onto trucks — no doubt the first part of a long journey to Japan.

In the late afternoon we went for a walk around Tarifa and spent some time at El Castillo Califal, the Castle of Califph, absorbing some of the local culture before heading back to Zahara de los Atuns. I was so excited at the prospect of swimming with schools of giant fish that I barely slept that night.

Back in Barbate the next morning, we ran along the main length of the *almadraba*, a wall of net nearly 2 miles long, on our way to the holding pen. As Luciano explained how everything worked, Maria did a good job of translating and relaying the information. Bluefin caught in outer chambers of the maze are herded into *la piscina*. The almadraba crew accomplishes this by raising and lowering various panels of the netting and driving the bluefin from one chamber to another using a most unlikely device: They tow a large piece of white sail canvas, stretched on a triangular frame, hanging down in the water behind a skiff. The crude decoy mimics an orca, and the bluefin swim

Below: Alberto and Maria Iriarte at the almadraba *in Barbate.*

Above: Harvey, José Luis Beistegui and Bill Boyce in the fish market at Tarifa.

quickly away into the desired pen. As we approached *la piscina*, we could see dorsal fins and tails cutting the surface and the bulge in the water as numerous giant tuna cruised close to the surface. Luciano took us over the outer wall of mesh, and then inside. The visibility was not good — perhaps only 30 feet — but it did not matter as the tuna poured past us like a school of VW Beetles, a stampede of marine bison. Alberto and Maria toured the whole pen while Bill and I, cameras rolling, hung out with the giant tuna.

The holding pen measured approximately 100 meters long by 75 meters wide by 30 meters deep. We did not see any other fish in the pen except giant bluefin tuna, though the divers had earlier removed a swordfish. Although we could see only 50 or so giant bluefin at a time, we were able to shoot from all angles. Conditioned to having divers around them, the tuna swam by closely. Bill and I carried still cameras as well, so we shot rolls of print and slide film. I could not get over the size of the giant tuna; most were in the 400- to 600-pound range, but several toads may well have topped 800.

I made nonstop mental notes about bluefin anatomy, observing body length, the vivid bronze band along the body below the dark back, the brightness of the yellow finlets, how the anal fin glowed silver and the angle at which the pectoral fins were set. I noticed some individual variation as well. One giant was lit up, glowing blue from head to tail. Another displayed a white tail lacking pigmentation. We did not see any tagged fish.

The current pushed us to the end of the pen, so we worked our way back to the middle. Normal swimming speed appeared to be 5 knots. The fish moved with ease and effortless grace, using quite a stiff swimming action, their powerful muscles transferring great energy to broad tails. At one point a body of clear water came through, and the visibility improved to 80 feet, which made for great shooting.

Luciano called us out after an hour, which had passed in a flash. I could have stayed there all day. Back on the workboat, Luciano was telling Maria about the other fish that get caught in the *almadraba*. Though the system proves quite selective and produces very little bycatch, the traps do catch a few white marlin, hammerhead and mako sharks, as well as up to 60 swordfish per season. Even orcas find their way into the pens occasionally.

Luciano respects orcas, which he considers the most intelligent creatures in the sea. When he works underwater repositioning gear or setting anchors, orcas sometimes swim next to him and watch what he's doing for long periods. In 25 years of working at the *almadraba*, he has never had reason to fear them, but they do give him work from time to time. He explained how a bull orca would go into the chambers, knowing exactly how to get through the maze and enter the holding pen. It would "stampede" the tuna, many of which would jump out of the pen only to be caught on the other side by female orcas waiting there. Some big tuna would burst the wall of the pen, allowing many others to escape.

The *almadraba* at Barbate enjoyed a good season, producing 1,500 metric tons of giant bluefin tuna, about one-sixth of the total Spanish quota as stipulated by the International Commission for the Conservation of Atlantic Tunas, the agency charged with governing highly migratory species such as tuna and billfish.

The following May, Bill and I returned to the *almadraba* in Barbate. This time we planned to dive with the giant bluefin tuna in the "death chamber" while the crew pulled up the bottom of the chamber. Many film crews had shot this from boats, but none — as far as José Luis knew — had dived with the tuna during the harvesting procedure.

We arrived in Barbate on May 15, greeted by 30-knot winds out of the east. It had been blowing for three days, and no one had been able to go out to the *almadraba*. We toured the maintenance yard and saw that Luciano kept the men busy mending nets, splicing rope, fixing buoys, chipping rust and cleaning anchors. The *almadraba* resembles a ship with a crew of about 120 men, and its captain, Vicente, is a distinguished looking gentleman, generally curt in speech and separated from the men. Luciano, contracted by the system's operator to maintain the system of pens, had been there so long that he had become the equivalent of a first lieutenant. He was the man all the others looked up to and respected.

On the morning of May 17, we got to the dock at Barbate at 6 a.m. as 100 other men boarded the workboats amid little chatter. They all knew their jobs. The charged

Opposite: Swordfish on Dolphin, *mixed media.*

Below: The vast expanse of the almadraba *lies 2 miles off the Barbate coast.*

atmosphere made me feel like I was participating in the start of an invasion. The men were anxious to get to work because poor weather had prevented them from landing any tuna for the past week. The sea was calm, but skies loomed cloudy in the semidarkness.

The few workboats with engines tow six "catcher" boats out to the *almadraba*. Once there, most of the work is done by paddling in and around the chambers in a labor-intensive process steeped in ritual and ceremony.

Our workboat entered the death chamber, and we waited for 1 1/2 hours while three divers, Luciano among them, checked the outer chambers for tuna. The other men watched and laughed while putting on their oilskins. A buzz went through the crew — tuna in the trap! Using the orca-imitation method, a boat herded fish from an outer chamber into the death chamber. Divers raised the end wall, passing the ropes up to the crew. A roar went up as they hauled up the wall of mesh to prevent the tuna from escaping. The men began chanting and pulling in unison.

There was another long wait. A group of tuna had been trapped in one of the outer chambers, and Vicente wanted to move them closer to the death chamber. So it was done. Vicente's crew paddled him over to our boat, and once aboard, he seemed satisfied that all was set. The death chamber held a ring of six workboats laid out in a hexagon. Three boats on our side of the chamber would pull up off the floor of the net while the crew on the opposite three boats faced the exhilarating job of gaffing bluefin tuna once they came within range. The gaff men definitely occupy the top of the seniority ladder, like marine matadors.

Vicente told us we could get in now that the net was ready to come up; it would take 20 minutes of hauling before the killing began. Each gaff man gripped a personal hand gaff made of forged steel, sharpened and shiny, with a leather wrist strap. Several other men wielded long-handled gaffs.

Overcast conditions made for poor lighting, but the water was clear blue. Maria kindly filmed topside for me, while Bill, Alberto, José Luis and I went into the death chamber. A large school of mackerel swam about unmolested by the tuna. At 60 feet I found the giant bluefin tuna slowly milling in a wide circle. I stayed with them as they went back and forth, round and round, in their ever-decreasing world. The tuna quickened their pace and colors began to change as they realized there was no way out. Vivid stripes appeared on their flanks and bellies, and the blue in their backs glowed as the level of excitement rose. Fins became erect as fish maneuvered and changed direction

constantly. They were avoiding the mesh wall, each other and me. I lost sight of Bill in the density of bodies, but could see the mesh coming up under me. Some of the tuna were breaking the surface, dragging trails of bubbles after them, adding to the visual excitement. I was getting superb footage of these charging fish, coming right at me, passing the camera by a foot. I swam up and pointed the camera at the yelling men as they hauled on the mesh. I got the distinct impression they wanted me out of the water, but pretending not to hear in the clamor and din, I slid back under the surface and continued filming the unfolding drama. And drama it was! Tuna of 300 to 700 pounds blistered past, all going in the same direction, so they generated their own whirlpool. I was swept away from my boat. Still the tuna did not bump into me, and I kept the camera rolling. The surface churned white with foam, and a tuna hit the mesh in front of me, snagging its jaw. It thrashed violently and tore free. Now it was definitely time to leave!

The men stopped hauling on the ropes and tied off the net with hooks. They watched as struggling fish ran out of room to swim and beat the water to a froth. Fins and tails zigzagged in the foam as this frenetic scene of death approached climax. There was no shouting or screaming, just the sound of water roaring like a waterfall.

Suddenly cheers went up, and the gaffing started. A gaff man leaned over and planted his steely point in the nearest tuna's cheek. The powerfully pumping tail propelled him sideways, but several marine matadors assisted their amigo, and soon the 500-pound tuna was manhandled upward and over the gunwale. The men's necks and arms bulged with exertion, faces contorted with strain amid yelling, grunting, screaming, dripping

Above: Front Runner, *acrylic on canvas. The leader of a pack of giants has its eye on a mackerel bait.*

Opposite: The ruins of the Roman municipium of Baelo Claudia lies just outside Barbate.

125

Below: Wearing his white hat, Vicente, captain of the almadraba, *directs the harvesting operation.*

Above: The equivalent of marine matadors haul in a 500-pound tuna. Photos by Bill Boyce.

water, sweat and blood. As each tuna slid into the boat, men deftly danced aside to allow the huge, swinging tail clear passage. A blow from that tail could break a leg.

I continued to shoot from the workboat, then went back into the water along the net to a catcher boat. Tuna thumped me as they passed. I wanted to get the angle of the fish being gaffed from the water, and Vicente had given me permission to go back in. While the carnage was appalling, the process was fascinating! Gaff men who got dragged into the maelstrom by kicking tuna would stay in the net, gaffing more fish and passing them on to their amigos in the boats. One man next to me sank his gaff into the head of a 700-pounder and got dragged to the other side of the pen. In the marine version of a bullring, men thrived on the action and drama, yet worshipped these fish in a biblical way. At the same time it was a show, with vast amounts of testosterone flying around. I filmed another gaff man in yellow oilskins getting dragged around underwater before crashing into the mesh and popping to the surface. The water was cloudy with blood, and a slick of oil from the dying tuna covered the surface. Those still alive swam around aimlessly, scarred from contact with the mesh and each other. Soon, they, too, fell to the gaff men — 286 giants in all.

Vicente stood like a statue watching the entire process, occasionally barking orders. Beside him stood a couple of Japanese men who may have been counting the fish pulled into each boat. It ended quickly — just another day in this centuries-old tradition, but an unforgettable experience for our camera crew. From a conservationist's or recreational angler's point of view, the death toll seemed horrendous. It was "blood and tears," said Maria, weeping for the fish. From a cultural point of view, the process remains artisan and traditional. The only nontraditional part was that played by the Japanese overseers, who clearly ran the show.

The catcher boats were towed back into the harbor as the crew hosed down the fish. The first boat went straight to the Japanese factory ship while the other two went to the icehouse. Maria and I went with one of these and filmed workers pouring crushed ice onto the catch, then we headed back to the Japanese ship. Here tuna were hoisted up in twos and threes. A group of three men verified the weights before sliding tuna across the bloody deck to the chop shop. A man with a chain saw cut off the heads and tails; the body continued on to groups of Oriental fish butchers, who expertly reduced the huge carcasses to four fillets in a matter of minutes without wasting a stroke or discarding an ounce of flesh. The heads went into a truck while backbones, hearts, gills, guts and gonads were all separated for specific uses. Only smaller tuna of 250 pounds were sent into the hold as whole fish.

We filmed the process for two hours, documenting every procedure, including those performed by two Spanish marine scientists who were taking tissue samples and recording biological data from each fish. Apart from the chain-saw operator and the scientists, everybody working on deck was Oriental.

The strategic location of the *almadrabas* in Barbate and Tarifa have resulted in fairly constant catches of bluefin tuna over the past few decades. However, *almadrabas* and *matanzas* farther inside the Mediterranean have seen rapidly declining catches. High-seas longliners and purse seiners continue to indiscriminately demolish the oceanic resources of highly migratory species. The fewer the fish, the more valuable they become.

Scientists from the Oceanographic Institute of Spain had requested access to the spawn-filled bluefin tuna for years to attempt to induce spawning in captivity. Finally they were making progress, and Aniceto Ramirez was allowing them to siphon off two or three dozen fish to be kept in a separate circular pen in hopes that the captive fish would get to work. The inability to distinguish the sex of the fish in the water, and therefore match an equal number of males and females, poses an inherent problem.

*Top: As the bottom of the pen is raised, the
tuna have little water to swim in. In their futile
attempt to escape, they beat the water into a
white froth. The result sounds like a waterfall.*

*Above: Harvey (blue wetsuit) gets a close look
at the Spanish tuna harvesting operation.
Photos by Bill Boyce.*

Off La Gomera, Canary Islands, Harvey films
a spearfish, which is foul-hooked in the tail.
The hook was removed and the spearfish
swam off in good condition.
Photo by Bill Boyce.

On the bright side, Japanese scientists have been able to induce spawning in captive bluefin, and yellowfin tuna have spawned in captivity in Panama.

It would seem appropriate to hold more adult tuna in captivity to induce spawning before they end up on the one-way trip to Japan. Surely, both Aniceto and his Japanese buyers realize this. On the other hand, this method of fishing excludes juveniles, recruiting only larger adults that have already spawned several times. Much criticism has been directed at French and Spanish purse-seine operators in the Mediterranean who harvest large numbers of juveniles in their nursery areas around the Balearic Islands.

While stocks survive, people like Dr. Barbara Block of the Tag-A-Giant (TAG) research program try to make a difference by obtaining remarkable new knowledge about bluefin tuna. The team hopes to have 1,000 electronically tagged tuna swimming in the North Atlantic by 2003, having already tagged 500 medium and giant bluefin tuna in the Gulf of Mexico, North Carolina, New England and the Mediterranean Sea.

MUCH TO LEARN ABOUT BLUEFIN

Through tagging programs and satellite tracking conducted by Dr. Barbara Block, we know that bluefin tuna spawn somewhere in the Gulf of Mexico in the spring, then migrate north through the Florida Straits, riding the Gulf Stream to summer feeding grounds off the northeast coast of the U.S. and Canada. Here, they fatten up on the abundant supply of herring and mackerel.

Bluefin may stay in the Western Atlantic for several seasons before crossing the North Atlantic on their way to Iceland and Norway, swinging south past the Bay of Biscay, Portugal and the southern coast of Spain. Some bluefin migrate through the Azores and enter the Mediterranean. Tagging results show these fish can travel 1,670 nautical miles in 90 days, sometimes swimming at depths of 3,000 feet.

Some bluefin complete the cycle and recross the Atlantic, entering the Eastern Caribbean before heading back to the Gulf of Mexico to spawn — making a round trip of at least 10,000 miles.

All along their migratory routes — particularly in international waters — bluefin tuna run the gauntlet of longlines and purse seines from many nations. As their numbers decline, the value of these fish keeps rising through the roof. In fact, the bluefin has become the most valuable animal on the planet, with Japanese buyers paying tens of thousands of dollars for fish in good condition with high fat content. A record-high price of $170,000 was recently paid for one large tuna! Is there any chance that they will survive exploitation?

Probably not, if the management systems in place today don't change in the very near future. The International Commission for the Conservation of Atlantic Tunas serves as the international body responsible for the management of this oceanic nomad, but only 22 nations are signatories. Most members of ICCAT represent various commercial interests that exploit bluefin tuna. Steeped with hypocrisy, this arrangement draws severe criticism from recreational user groups — to the extent that author Carl Safina (*Song for the Blue Ocean*) characterizes the commission as the "International Conspiracy to Catch All Tunas."

ICCAT currently attempts to manage eastern and western bluefin tuna as two separate stocks. Knowing the bluefin's ability to cover great distances, however, many feel it's unlikely that separate populations exist in specific ocean basins. At this writing, researchers are conducting DNA analysis and pop-up tagging of bluefin tuna from the Western Atlantic, Eastern Atlantic and Mediterranean to determine whether distinct population groups exist.

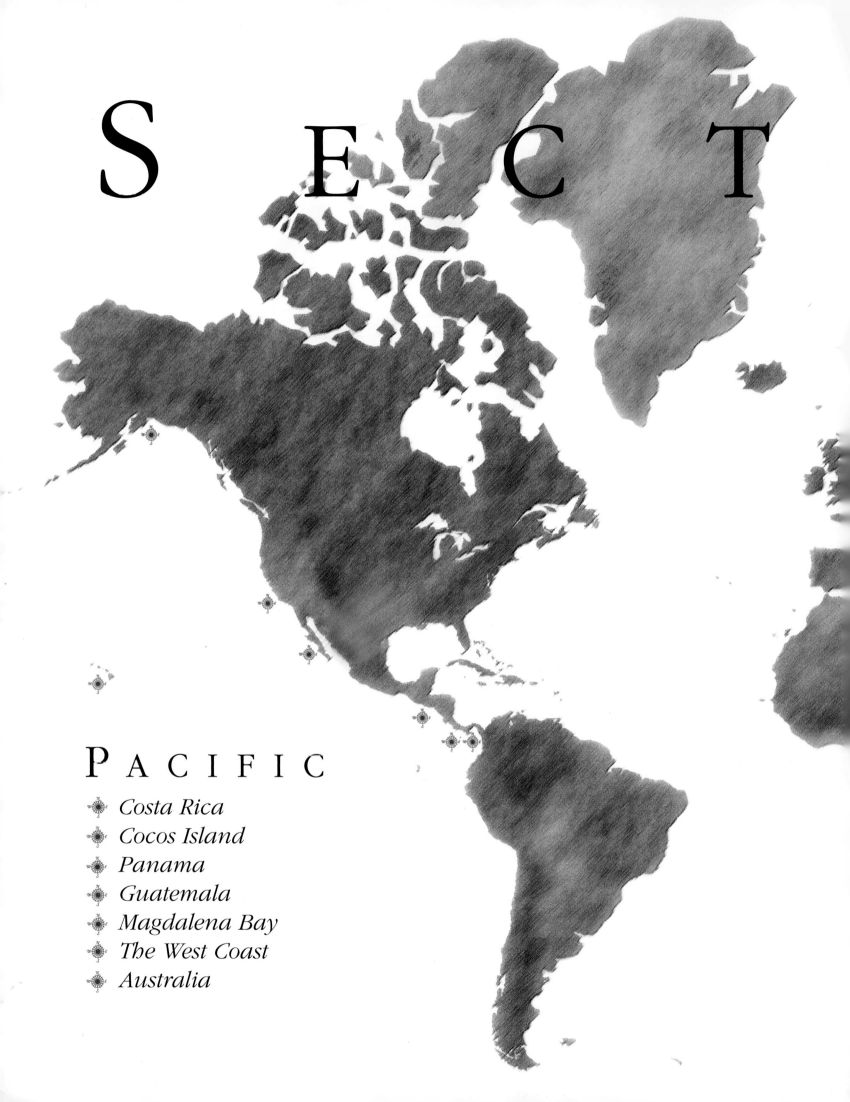

S E C T

P A C I F I C

CHAPTER 12

Opposite: Beach Patrol, *mixed media,*
portrays a roosterfish in chase of mullet. In the
background are king angels, blue striped
snapper, Pacific horseye jacks and a
whitetip reef shark.

COSTA RICA
First Look at a New Ocean

Game fishing on the Pacific coast of Costa Rica opened up in the mid-1980s with the building of a new marina in Flamingo Bay, in the northwestern province of Guanacaste. Before this, no modern facilities existed to cater to those who wanted to ply these prolific waters. One of the first operations on the scene was Flamingo Bay Pacific Charters, started by Floridian Paul Hirschman and his partners.

I had met Paul at a Gulf and Caribbean Fisheries Conference in Bermuda in 1986, where he gave a talk about the potential of sport fishing in Costa Rica. His presentation convinced me, and with the help of Scotty Boyd of Fort Lauderdale, I put together a trip in July 1988.

Though I never did much diving off Flamingo Bay, this was an important chapter in my life, because it gave me my first exposure to the Pacific and the new varieties of species I needed to add to my portfolio for authenticity in game-fish art. Here I got my first look at striped marlin, black marlin, Pacific sailfish and a number of inshore species, including almaco jacks, roosterfish, Pacific dog snapper and an assortment of reef fish.

We stayed in the well-appointed Hotelera Playa Flamingo — a short walk from the marina, which was marked by two long seawalls, built from loosely piled rocks to help combat the ever-present Pacific ground swell. In our group were fellow Jamaicans John and Jenny Greaves, their youngest daughter, Noni, my fiancee, Gillian, Capt. Bob DeHart and his wife, Carol.

While the girls settled in, John, Bobby and I went for a half-day of trolling on the *Gamefisher II* with Capt. Richard Chellimi and mate "Junior." I will never forget those first few minutes. The baits and teasers had not been in the water 30 seconds when a doubleheader of sailfish came up. Bob and I caught one each. It continued like that for the rest of the afternoon, and we caught 16 out of 20 bites. When you are used to having one or two blue marlin bites per day in the Caribbean, having so many fish in the baits is thrilling. The experience gave us all a chance to correct and perfect our angling skills.

This trip also marked the first time I implemented catch-and-release in my personal fishing. At the time in Jamaica, we still boated every marlin we caught. But what were you going to do with 15 or 20 sailfish caught in a day? Stack them up in the boat and

give them away at the dock? There would not be many left after a couple of years if they were all boated, so during the next four days we caught and released 107 sailfish from about 200 bites, with 29 releases on our best day. Everyone caught his fill. I was overloaded with new experiences and was anxious to get these images of leaping sailfish on paper and canvas. But I had still not seen a black marlin.

I returned to Costa Rica a number of times in 1989 and '90 with a variety of friends from Jamaica and Florida. I fished with Richard a couple more times on the *Gamefisher II*, chalking up tremendous numbers of sailfish releases and eventually my first black marlin. That fish — an estimated 350-pounder tagged and released on July 4, 1989 — was a superb jumper that kept me busy for an hour on 30-pound gear.

In 1990, I fished five days with Capt. Laurie Wright on the *French Look*, a 46-foot Merritt owned by Jean Paul Richard. Jean Paul was trying for a sailfish record on 4-pound tackle with his team of Laurie, his wife, Julie Wright, and mate Kelly Wade.

Above: Profile of a Pacific sailfish.

Opposite: Two Sails and Dorado, *mixed media.*

Laurie kindly spent a lot of time coaching me in the art of finessing big fish on light tackle. We started out with 12-pound test, went down to 8-pound, then 6-pound, and ended up catching a couple of sails on 4-pound test. I was hooked! Light tackle became a fad for me for a few years in the Pacific. Though I lost a lot of fish, the few I did catch were really special. In addition to the many light-tackle sails in Costa Rica, I managed blacks on 20- and 16-pound-test in Panama and two striped marlin on 8-pound-test at Cocos Island.

Though many well-known anglers such as Raleigh Werking and Jerry Dunaway were breaking all sorts of records on ultralight tackle, I felt I lost touch with the fish on anything less than 8-pound-test. With 8-pound, I could comfortably put heat on a fish and make it do things. With lighter line, I felt that the boat fought too much of the battle, with the angler relegated to simply reeling in the slack and paying the bills.

One of my favorite paintings at that time was *Jumped Him Off*, which came from a morning spent trying to catch a black with Laurie using live skipjacks for both teasers and bait. I jumped off two blacks in quick succession after glorious aerial displays, and broke off a third. The Costa Rican experiences inspired a lot of other work, including pieces that portray schools of spinner and spotted dolphins mixed in with both sailfish and big yellowfin tuna, a phenomenon rarely witnessed in my home waters of the Caribbean.

In 1991 and 1992, I fished with some of the other captains in Flamingo Bay, including Danny Timmons on the *Can't Touch Dis*, Bubba Carter on the *Tijereta* and Tim Choate on the *Magic*, one of several boats he owned and operated in Costa Rica at the time. (Tim moved his operation to Guatemala in the mid-'90s, amid growing concerns about the Costa Rican government's approach to billfish management. At the time, plans were under way that would allow commercial longliners to operate in the country's rich billfish grounds.) Fishing with Tim was a real education. He is as good an angler as you will find anywhere, and is always ready to share experiences or teach new techniques.

Perhaps the greatest development during my visits to Costa Rica's Flamingo Coast was that doors were opened for future trips to Cocos Island, a rarely visited but ecologically rich volcanic peak 300 miles off the country's coast. Around Cocos the marlin fishing was reputed to be outstanding, with striped marlin outnumbering sailfish 5-to-1. Blues and blacks were also said to be common catches, making the prospect of a grand slam excellent. Jerry Dunaway's mothership operation, the *Madam* and the *Hooker*, were set to fish Cocos Island for several consecutive summers, so I made plans to be a part of those expeditions.

Subsequent trips to Costa Rica in 1993, '94, '95 and '96 were all visits to this magical island (see Chapter 13), and it was on my first expedition here that I met underwater cameraman Rick Rosenthal. At the time he was in the process of filming a documentary about life in the surface waters of the tropical eastern Pacific Ocean, based around the movements of a drifting log and its associated marine life. The result was a tremendous documentary, produced by the BBC and the Discovery Channel, called *Hunters of the Sea Wind*. This set the standard by which all other documentaries on the tropical open ocean will be judged.

My experiences during that first visit to Cocos Island ignited my imagination like never before, and it was on my next visit there in 1994 that my efforts to film free-swimming billfish began in earnest.

Amigos, *mixed media. Dolphin and tuna often*
interact in the tropical eastern Pacific.

CHAPTER 13

*Opposite: Harvey films a 30-plus-foot
whale shark off Cocos Island.
Photo by Wayne Hasson.*

*Below: The live-aboard dive boat
Okeanos Aggressor anchors below the
rain forest and scenic waterfall of Cocos.*

COCOS ISLAND
Birthplace of a New Passion

Because of its isolation 300 miles from the coast and its status as a national park, Cocos Island has remained uninhabited except for small groups of visiting researchers and a few park rangers. Only 4 miles long but with rain forest-covered peaks reaching 2,200 feet, the island presents an imposing image. Swirling clouds and frequent rain often engulf the peaks, creating many beautiful waterfalls that cascade off the high cliffs and into the sea. Thousands of sea birds roost here, including frigate birds, fairy terns, and red-footed, brown and masked boobies.

Because it has a reliable supply of fresh water, Cocos Island has always attracted mariners. For three centuries it was the pirates; countless stories exist of fortunes buried in the island's interior. For today's visiting divers and naturalists, the real treasure of Cocos is found beneath the water's surface. Because the island is a fist of volcanic rock sticking up out of the Cocos Ridge in the middle of the eastern Pacific Ocean, the ocean currents swirling past the steep cliffs bring nutrients, baitfish and large numbers of pelagic predators. On any given day, you can expect to encounter billfish, tuna, manta rays and stingrays, dolphins, whales, turtles and a variety of sharks.

Having been plundered by commercial lobster fishermen, spear fishermen and longliners for years, Cocos exists now as a national park with a no-take zone that extends 5 miles out from the island. This zone was established primarily to protect the scalloped hammerhead sharks that serve as the main attraction for visiting divers.

My first visit to Cocos was aboard the *Can't Touch Dis* with Jim Robinson, who had arranged to meet up with Wayne Hasson on the *Okeanos Aggressor*, one of the live-aboard dive boats that visit the island twice a month. Wayne is a famous underwater photographer, entrepreneur and managing founder of the Aggressor Dive Fleet worldwide. We fished enough to sample what Cocos had to offer, and I caught a grand slam (blue marlin, striped marlin and sailfish) on July 11, 1993. We caught several other blues and stripers, but spent most of the time diving with Wayne.

That visit was the first of five to the island, with the next three occurring on Jerry Dunaway's *Madam* and *Hooker* mothership operation. The beauty of Jerry's outfit was that I could fish for six hours a day and still complete two or three dives, including some at night. This sort of program made for an action-packed day, especially when you consider the pace of the fishing we experienced with Capt. Trevor Cockle and mates Randy Baker, Mikey Deighan and Kurt Schloderer.

Since the park boundaries extend 5 miles from the island, we spent most days to the west and south of the island looking for striped marlin, blue marlin, sailfish and the occasional black. Grand slams were always a possibility, but striped marlin provide the fastest action — usually at least 10 fish a day. Because of the prolific numbers of striped marlin, I took advantage of good weather during my first trip with the *Hooker* in 1994 and jumped off the boat to dive with and film free-swimming marlin for the first time. I could never have dreamed how this decision would shape my life and career over the next several years.

As I entered the water on that first dive, my heart raced. I can only imagine my eyes wide with anticipation as I cleared the cloud of bubbles and faced for the first time a free, living, feeding marlin silhouetted against the silver surface. The striped marlin was swimming straight at me, its neon-blue tail sweeping from side to side in its haste to overtake the teaser. The fish swept overhead just 2 feet above me, pectorals spread wide like a jet plane as it repeatedly grabbed at the teaser. I fired off a whole roll of film in a minute as the 200-pound marlin swam around me and charged the strip baits the crew presented.

With the boat stationary, I continued to free dive as Randy and Kurt cast the teasers well over my head and retrieved them quickly toward the boat. The marlin wheeled around and chased the bait, coming right toward me again. It passed my right side so closely I could have touched it, its blue eye rolling to glance at me as it followed the teaser.

For years I had watched marlin suddenly appear behind a bait and grab it, but I was able to see only the dorsal fin, the tip of the bill and a flurry of spray. Beneath it was a brown or black shadow, distorted by the foamy surface. Here before me in living, glowing color was a sight few anglers get to see.

I made a few mistakes on my first dives. On one of my earliest attempts, a marlin came up on the short right teaser, and I went in while the boat was still in gear, giving myself too short a time to adjust and face the fish. Consequently, it was a very close encounter indeed, with the marlin sidestepping me with great agility as it blazed by in a flurry of neon blue and swirling bubbles. We learned to slow the boat down to neutral, as you would when fly-fishing, and to wear a heavyweight belt — 15 pounds at least — to pull me under the bubbles and the boat's wake. I also switched to using tanks; I got much better results with my filming efforts, and the exhaust bubbles did not spook the marlin.

When everything worked and the marlin teased in well, it was a most exciting and memorable experience. A hungry striped marlin comes streaking in behind a teaser with fins folded and a neon-blue tail — awesome! Then they would break sharply, their fins open and stripes "turned on" as if a switch had been flicked. This was definitely more exciting than catching them!

The more I dived with the stripers, the more confident I became and the more attention I paid to their feeding behavior instead of worrying about their reaction to me. Anglers and laymen around the world have preconceived ideas about how billfish feed. Many believe they use their bills either to spear or stun bait before returning to eat the meal. Yet on my initial encounter in Cocos — or on any subsequent dive anywhere in the world, for that matter — I have yet to see any billfish species use that behavior. This suggested that the bill is primarily a streamlining adaptation, perhaps used occasionally for offense or defense. It also suggested that anglers, even successful ones, still had much to learn about the way billfish behave under the surface.

What initially intrigued me most about marlin feeding behavior was the fishes' astounding accuracy. The marlin would open their mouths just enough to inhale the teaser or lure. They got it every time, and always stopped to chew on their catch, usually with their heads up at about a 30-degree angle. The marlin would then swallow the

Below: Wayne Hasson has proven to be one of the world's best underwater photographers.

Above: Jerry Dunaway fights a striped marlin on 12-pound tippet aboard the Hooker.

*A striped marlin grabs the teaser off Cocos
Island. This fish provided Harvey with his first
close encounter with free-swimming billfish.*

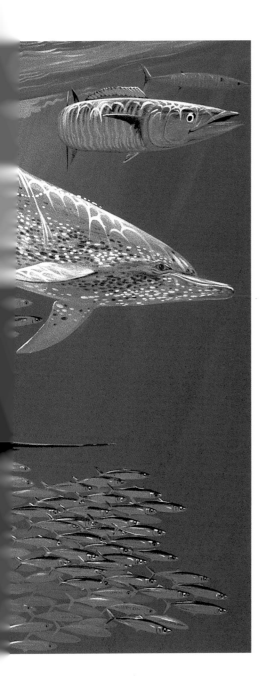

Left: Cocos Motion, *acrylic on canvas, portrays a classic Cocos scene — a bait ball surrounded by dolphins, sailfish, wahoo and rainbow runner.*

Bottom: A scalloped hammerhead and creole fish.

bait with a sharp inhalation of water. In the early days of filming marlin underwater, we did not have access to live bait as an alternative to the strips or dead bait we used, so I observed a great deal of chewing, probably because the mate was trying to pull the bait away from the marlin.

We also raised a fair number of sailfish in Cocos, often in conjunction with stripers. In contrast to the brilliant neon blues seen on a striped marlin, the sails were generally dark — often completely black — and with dorsal and pelvic fins erect, the sailfish looked huge in the water. To specifically target sails, we obtained permission from head ranger Joaquim Alvarado to troll teasers close to the cliffs for sailfish. In those same spots, we received the unexpected bonus of giant wahoo.

We raised a tremendous number of wahoo, sometimes over a hundred in just two hours. They came up on the teasers like striped missiles, skyrocketing 15 feet or more right behind the boat. With the verdant walls of tropical jungle in the background, they made a wonderful sight. It was even more special when you consider how rarely one gets a chance to closely observe free-swimming wahoo. Many times I would jump in with a sailfish teased up to a daisy chain and find myself surrounded by a dozen wahoo, as well as several big rainbow runner.

The billfish were only part of the attraction to Cocos Island. At various locations, groups of scalloped hammerhead sharks congregate during the day, often coming in close to the rocks to be cleaned by attentive barberfish and king angelfish. Because of the shy nature of these big sharks, I learned to stay concealed among the huge boulders at the base of the cliff. When one approached, I would wait until the last second before taking a photo; the flash would scare it off immediately. Other times, it was possible to get below the big schools of hammerheads and take the classic shot with several dozen sharks in the frame, silhouetted against the surface.

Because of the large numbers of sharks present, it should come as no surprise that we saw a great deal of commercial longline activity around Cocos Island. I saw several high-seas, foreign-flagged longliners unloading container loads of sharks in the commercial port of Puntarenas on the mainland. Small Costa Rican vessels also fished for sharks near the island or in the anchorage at Chatham Bay, despite the presence of the rangers. I saw several hammerheads with longline hooks and trailing leaders on each of my visits to Cocos.

Big silky sharks and a similar species, the Galapagos shark, also provided plenty of entertainment. They often accompanied the yellowfin tuna that would sweep in to the rocks, looking for easy prey. The silkies would get excited when they joined a feeding opportunity, usually created by the tunas and dolphins.

The dolphins would locate a school of mackerel scads (*Decapterus sanctae-helenae*) and herd them to the surface, where they would consume them in a flurry of spray and bubbles. If the tuna were close by, they would get in on the act. In 1993, one such bait ball in Chatham Bay lasted long enough for every predator in the area to join the melee — a swirling cavalcade of dolphin, tuna, sharks, wahoo, sailfish, rainbow runner and

*Right: Harvey's first whale shark meanders by
fellow diver, Kent Ullberg.*

Below: Dolphin Tuna Tango, *acrylic on canvas,
a piece inspired by an unforgettable experience
in Chatham Bay.*

jacks. I did not have a camera at the time, but the experience inspired several paintings.

Another memorable incident occurred later that afternoon in the same location. The bottlenose dolphins had gathered a small group of mackerel scad from the deep, and the water grew loud with their constant jabbering. As they ascended from the depths, I could see what was happening. A school of a dozen scad had somehow gotten close to a dolphin's neck and chest between its pectoral fins and could not be dislodged, even by the vigorous gyrations of the host dolphin. Its fellow dolphins followed closely, but did not attempt to grab the baitfish — they appeared undecided. Suddenly a group of 150-pound yellowfin tuna swooped in and showed no such hesitation. One of them crashed into the left flank of the dolphin while aiming for the scad, disrupting the pressure wave around the dolphin, and the scads showered in all directions. The dolphin and tuna consumed them instantly, and I could clearly hear the popping sound of the tuna catching the bait.

From time to time, the plankton would be thick in Chatham Bay, attracting lots of planktoniverous species, such as green jacks, sergeant majors, steel pompano, rainbow chub, cortez chub and creole fish. Big manta rays also came into the shallows. I took advantage of the shallow water and distracted animals by getting close to these huge animals. One manta was an unusual color — nearly all black, except for a small white patch on its belly, similar to an underwater stealth bomber.

I found it rewarding to be able to swim among these huge animals without spooking

WHALE SHARK · COCOS ISLAND

Left: One of the many manta rays that converge at Cocos.

Below: Kent Ullberg and Harvey take a break from the fast-paced fishing and diving schedule aboard the Hooker.

them. If the water was deep enough, the mantas would sometimes do a complete summersault in front of me, exposing their white bellies and then coming back upright at the surface. If I stayed there quietly and watched them swim by, they would get close, but if I swam after them to get a closer shot they would accelerate away with ease, dipping and curling their wing tips alternately, as if in a dance routine.

Another giant creature I encountered for the first time at Cocos was the whale shark. It was early morning, and I had just entered the water and dropped to 30 feet to wait for the other divers. I took one shot of some blue jacks to make sure the camera was working properly, and then noticed a 25-foot whale shark coming slowly along the drop-off straight toward me. I could not believe my luck — a full tank of air, a full roll of film and great visibility. Kent Ullberg was next to me, and I took as many shots of him with the fish as I could to give some idea of the whale shark's size. I had been advised that these sharks spook easily, so we just kept close and admired this huge creature without attempting to touch it.

The whale shark made several circles around us and allowed close inspection by the other divers before wandering off down the rock wall. It was a tremendous and inspirational experience, and I could not wait to get some of this down on paper. As it turned out, this was more difficult than I had imagined because of the shark's sheer size. You really need to paint it life size to give any impression of its grand proportions. Additionally, because a whale shark is always accompanied by a school of small fish such as remoras, black jacks, golden trevally, blue runners and even cobia, a lot of detail, color, movement and drama must be included in portraits of this otherwise placid animal.

Opposite: Whale Shark at Dirty Rock, *watercolor.*

With all this action and variety, it was easy to get carried away with the big pelagics at Cocos Island and to overlook the abundance and beauty around the rocks. The biomass of reef fish was astounding; we sighted far too many species to list here. Whitetip reef sharks were also abundant, often lying in untidy groups on the sandy bottom, like logs at a lumberyard. When a diver approached, they would unwind in a distinct order, the top one leaving first, the bottom shark last. We saw many spotted eagle rays, as well as placid, majestic marble rays, which could be handled without spooking. There was so much to see and absorb, I had a hard time deciding where to look. And the lobsters — they were everywhere!

Above: Whitetip reef sharks hunt in a rock pile.

Opposite: Scalloped Hammerhead, *watercolor, shows barberfish (yellow and black) and king angelfish (dark blue) cleaning a hammerhead at Cocos.*

At cleaning stations, we observed barberfish, a delicate species of butterfly fish, clean hammerhead sharks in organized fashion. A hammerhead would peel off the school some distance above the rocks, sweep in and slow down for 10 seconds or so while it was obscured by a yellow cloud of busy, fluttering barberfish. The shark would then accelerate away, making space for a replacement. If left undisturbed, a conveyor belt of hammerhead bodies would come through the cleaning station.

We saw many more examples of cleaning stations along the rocks, as well as several hunting partnerships between two species. The fact is, Cocos Island stands as a powerful magnet for a naturalist. It is as if Nature has crammed a quart of life into a pint-size bottle — so rich, plentiful, vibrant, colorful and inspirational is this location. Because of its prolific waters, Cocos has attracted the attention of a number of wildlife-documentary production companies. These have enabled the treasures of this unique place to be brought into people's lives on a regular basis, through television and now through IMAX cinematography.

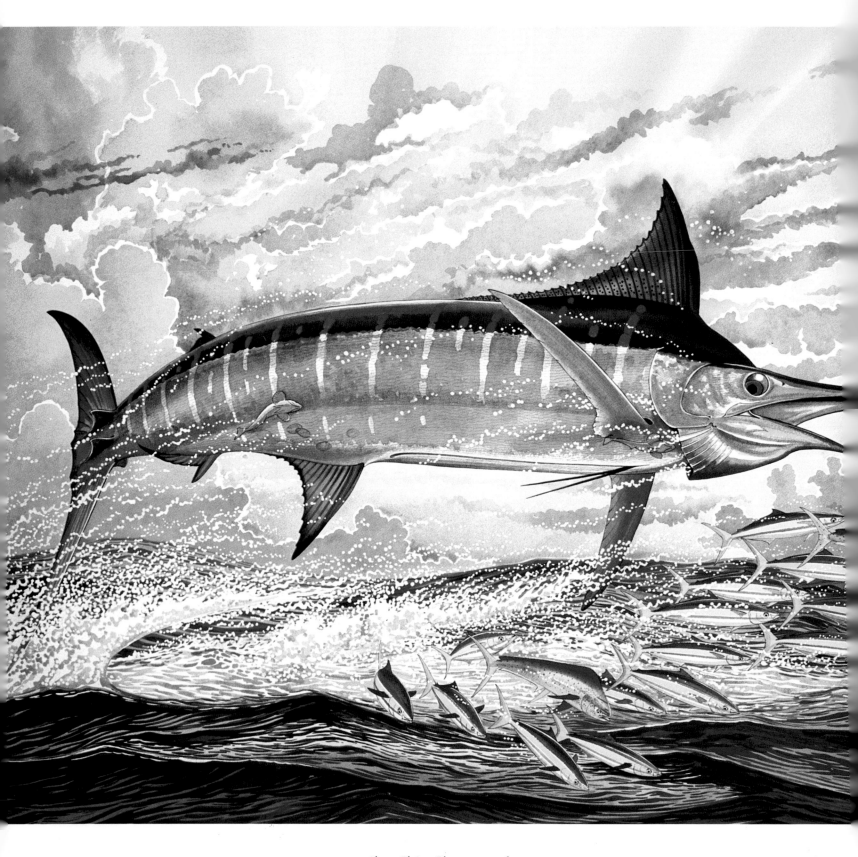

Above: Flying Blue, *watercolor.*
This is a sight seen often on the Zane Grey Reef,
where a blue or black marlin explodes on the
resident rainbow runner and dorado.

Opposite: A Tropic Star crew releases a
400-pound black.

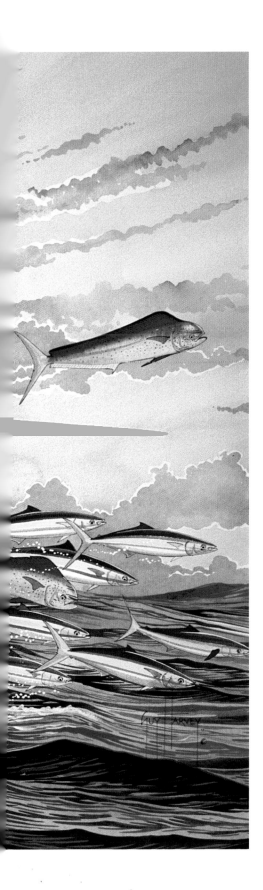

CHAPTER 14

PANAMA
Black Marlin on Zane Grey Reef

Serving as a sort of geological umbilical between Central and South America, Panama is fortunate to have beautiful shorelines lining both its Caribbean and Pacific coasts. Having spent so many years fishing and diving in the Caribbean, though, I concentrated in the past decade on expeditions to the eastern Pacific. Much of that time I stayed at Tropic Star Lodge, a fantastic fishing resort at Piñas Bay owned by Terri and Mike Andrews. Raleigh Werking told me of the fantastic fishing he enjoyed there during Noriega's regime, but I didn't get a chance to visit until 1991. Since then, I've been back 19 times.

Tropic Star Lodge is nestled above the beach with gardens that merge with the pristine Darien jungle, receding into the majestic mountain ranges in the background. An awe-inspiring place, Piñas Bay boasts rivers and estuaries, trees that fill the sky, birds, parrots, monkeys, snakes and even Darien Indians in small dugout canoes who still shoot fish with bows and arrows. Many who visit Tropic Star compare it with walking into a *National Geographic* magazine article, or being on a *Wild Discovery* film shoot.

Eleanor Armstrong leads the lodge's office in Panama City, while South Africa's Hennie and Ursula Marias head up the on-site management team. The team does an excellent job of keeping downtime to a minimum, especially when you consider the utter isolation of the place — there's not a road within 100 miles.

Perhaps the most impressive facet of Tropic Star Lodge, though, is the impact it and its owners have had on the Panamanian government. Through hard work and determination, the Andrews — with the help of lawyer and close friend, Marcus Ostrander — successfully lobbied the country's government to create a "recreational fishing only" zone around Piñas Bay in 1998. Panama declared all billfish, dorado and wahoo in the area for recreational use only and placed a ban on commercial operations. A similar law was passed in Guatemala a few years earlier. This sort of long-term planning for conservation will surely help marine resources recover from the excessive levels of exploitation that we so frequently see worldwide. If only other countries could see how

Right: The crew of the Hooker *wires a spectacular black marlin for the Johnny Morris group.*

Below: On the patio at Tropic Star Lodge, Kent Ullberg works on a clay mold of a black marlin, while Harvey sketches some action seen that day.

much more valuable to an economy these resources are alive than simply as a source of protein.

The fact is, fishermen have spent untold fortunes to visit the rich waters of Piñas Bay for decades. The big draw: black marlin, and plenty of them. Although I caught my first three blacks in Costa Rica in 1989 and another four in Australia in 1990, I've gained most of my experience with the species at Tropic Star, fishing along the famous Zane Gray Reef. On my first trip there, I was amazed at the amount of fish visible just at the surface of the reef. At sunrise, the surface would come alive as huge schools of bonito, rainbow runner and jacks consumed the baitfish constantly moving past the reef, led by the strong north-flowing current. Bait was always available and fun to catch — you never knew what would take a feather in these waters — and often catching the bait ended up a battle itself.

The green color and poor clarity of the water surprised me, and influenced me to not dive here until several years later. So the first dozen or so expeditions were simple fishing trips. Every trip was memorable, though some of the best expeditions were with Kent Ullberg; we both used our interaction with black marlin as reference for future works of art.

I have spent a lot of time pulling live bonito for black marlin on the reef. On my best day I caught and released three blacks, though many anglers have done better. The fish were not big — averaging 300 pounds — though Panama's blacks will often top 500 or even 600 pounds. A couple of blacks estimated in the 1,000-pound ball park have been released here, but Australia's Great Barrier Reef offers a more reliable source for large black marlin.

At Tropic Star, I fish mostly with an excellent captain named Isauro and his mate, Olivio. I generally use 50- and 30-pound line for the blacks, but I've also managed to catch a couple on 20-pound-test while trolling for sailfish. The black marlin stands as a formidable adversary on any tackle, and while it does not possess the speed of the blue marlin, its excels in the jumping department. The long bill, big head, broad shoulders, wide pectoral fins, dark back and bronze flanks all are pushed clear of the water by a big propeller and a heart of steel. The display of power is an angler's dream, but these days I much prefer to have a camera in my hand at such times than a rod.

If you fish long enough around the reef, you will see the black marlin working on the schools of bonito and rainbow runner. When a black stalks them, the bonito stop feeding and bunch up tightly, forming a dark mass in the water. Then with an explosion of

spray, the bonito flee in all directions, but usually one goes cartwheeling across the sky and another skitters across the surface uncontrollably for brief seconds before the marlin spins around to scoop up both injured fish. Possibly, the marlin has gone in with that mighty bill and used it to bat at the bonito, turning to pick up the injured fish. Yet none of my underwater experiences with hundreds of billfish have shown this to be standard behavior. The rainbow runners will greyhound as a school — an unforgettable sight — when a black marlin is after them. Predator/prey interactions such as these are abrupt and savage, but they make the very best subject matter for game-fish paintings.

I never got to dive with a black marlin in Piñas Bay because of the poor water clarity, but I have dived extensively there with sailfish, both teased up and balling *anchovetas*. The bait balls of *anchovetas* start appearing in late April and usually stay through May. They can be found generally to the south from Piñas Bay along the coast, where deep water is close to shore off Guayabo and Cocolita Reef. Any given bait ball will have a circle of attentive predators, and typically a single species of predator dominates each ball, such as sailfish at one ball or tuna at another. Jacks and sharks also stalk the *anchovetas*.

When action at the reef quiets down, anglers have the option of trolling out to the 100-fathom line, where a super grand slam of black, blue and striped marlin and sailfish represents a daily possibility. As with anywhere on this coast, you'll find many floating

Alex Harvey fought this 400-pound black marlin for 65 minutes unaided before receiving assistance with the catch.

logs carried from the south by the current. Huge derelict trees provide shelter for bait, so the dorado, rainbow runner, small yellowfin tuna and jack crevalle swim thick here. Offshore in cleaner water, I dived under these logs all day long; they serve as an oasis in the featureless blue world of pelagic animals. The endless blue water of underwater paintings can be monotonous, but by including logs, bait schools, foam and the surface I am able to authentically add drama and so portray a glimpse in the life history of these animals.

I prefer to fish Piñas Bay in January each year, when the offshore fishing offers a reliable alternative to fishing the reef. Often yellowfin tuna and big blue marlin can be found among the endless schools of dorado. These yellow nuisances can be so numerous that anglers often opt to pull only teasers and then present a hooked bait to a particularly large dorado, blue marlin or sailfish as they appear in the spread.

In March of 1998, I joined Andy Byatt, a producer working for the BBC Natural History Unit, filming life in the oceans for a BBC documentary called *The Blue Planet.* Andy wanted to film marine life on seamounts off Central America, so the Zane Grey Reef came to mind, and we joined forces at Tropic Star Lodge for two weeks of filming. I had prepared for this expedition by taking a Nitrox course, as well as doing a number of deep dives.

After all my years of fishing at the reef, it was going to be quite an experience to dive it. Mike Andrews and many other spearfishermen had dived and shot fish over the reef, but no one had really explored the pinnacle in the way we were able to do. On our first day out, it was flat calm, and we located the pinnacles on Capt. Jimmy Davis' boat, the *Madrugador.* We dropped a heavy weight plus 300 feet of rope and a big orange marker buoy. To our dismay, the rope was stretched horizontally in the current, and the buoy was pulled below the surface, with a rooster tail of foam pouring off it. Well, so much for that — we had to wait an entire week before the current eased up enough for us to dive.

In the meantime, we went 25 miles to the south and dived on a small pinnacle called Cocalita Reef, just a mile off the coast and a fishing hot spot in its own right. Jimmy had taken me there in 1997, so I knew what to expect. At the surface and for 50 feet down, the water remains warm and green, with only a few feet of visibility. But as you descend, you reach colder, clear water. A large school of big Pacific barracuda and numerous Pacific almaco jacks, also known as amberjack — a very inquisitive fish — greeted us on our first dive. Marked by a burnished metallic sheen, bronze with gold and pink and a dark stripe through their eyes and up toward their shoulders, these stern-looking fellows will escort you for an entire dive and serve as great companions.

On many subsequent dives, I would take down a ziplock bag full of bonito chunks and feed these fish. In no time, I would have 30 big fellows all over me swirling and jostling each other for food. Diving with big fish that are unafraid of humans proved to be a superb experience.

The up-current (southern) side of the pinnacle always provided the best action. Groups of big crimson snappers, some large Pacific dog snappers and itinerant mullet snappers hung out with the horse-eye jacks like big kids at a playground, looking for someone to bully. The exposed canine teeth and red eyes gave the mullet snapper the look of a tough street fighter. Big schools of jack crevalle and bonito would zoom in and out of the green gloom above us while we took footage of the blizzard of small reef fish among the rocks, gorgonians and sea fans.

As the current slackened, we were able to dive on the Cocalita Reef twice a day, for six days, so we became quite familiar with it. Andy and professional underwater cameraman Tom Fitz were able to obtain some unique footage, but after a week's wait it was time to try the Zane Grey Reef again.

Raging Bull, *watercolor.*
Harvey estimates the water around Zane Grey
Reef holds more 50-plus-pound dorado than
any other in the world.

Double Down, *acrylic on canvas.*
In a common scene off Panama, a pair of sails
chase a school of frigate mackerel.

Andy and I went down the marker line first. In a 1-knot current, I pulled myself down through the green layer with some anxiety. Almaco jacks and snappers appeared all around us. Finally, the water turned clear and cool at 80 feet, and I started filming Andy as he descended. I could hardly see him — he was almost completely covered in almaco jacks! He anchored the roop at 170 feet, on the craggy-looking pinnacle of rock.

The visibility was incredible. I could see all the way down the rocky slope to the sand plain at the bottom, at 350 feet. Below us the vermilion snappers were thick, while above us the almaco jacks continued to gather and block my view. I let the camera roll continuously as there was so much going on, so much to see. Big fish came by to look us over. We didn't even have to swim; they all came to us. We only had nine minutes of bottom time before we had to start our ascent on the rope, accompanied all the way by our faithful companions. As we got closer to the surface, the visibility deteriorated.

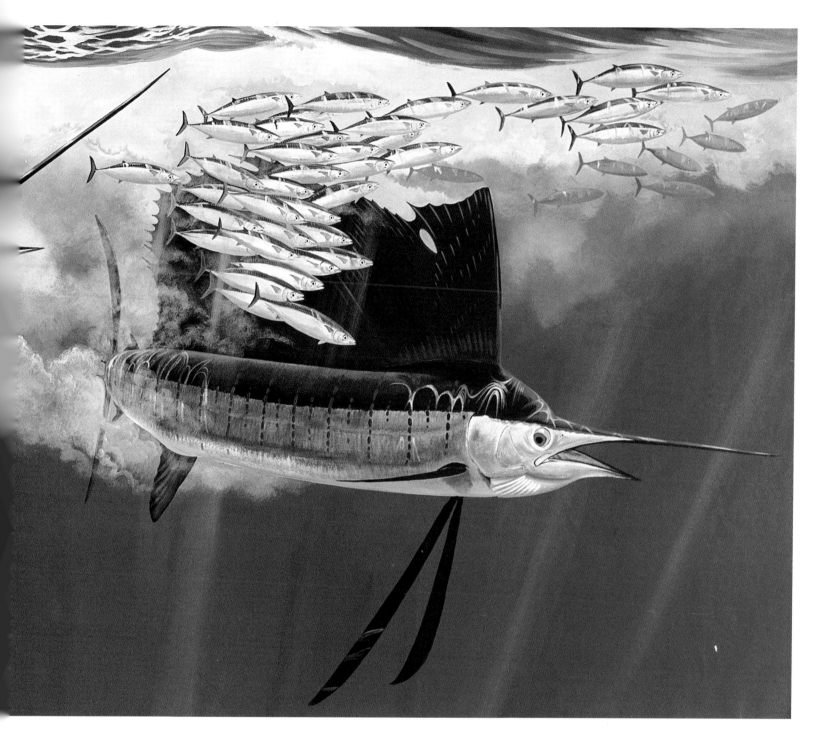

Bonitos, rainbow runners and dorado flashed by as we made our decompression stops, blowing off our nitrogen.

After our four-hour surface interval, we headed back down. Knowing what to expect, I looked beyond the almaco jacks that had befriended us to see big Pacific dog snapper, broomtail grouper, African pompano, golden trevally, manta rays, scalloped hammerheads and the occasional silvertip shark.

While Tom was filming all this, I took in the layout of the pinnacle. Two distinct rock formations with two pinnacles formed the southern ridge, while the northern peak had a rounded, almost flattened top. The surface of the rock was bare with a scattering of small white coralline encrustations. We didn't see nearly the number of small reef fish as were present at Cocalita Reef — just a few creole fish and king angels, with no baitfish in any quantity. I wondered what the many almaco jacks and snappers fed on. Perhaps they go offshore at night to feed, presumably on squid, and return to the reef during the day for safety.

During the next three days, we did two more dives per day on the reef. I got used to the narcosis and could spend more time appreciating the sights around us. We dived on the third (northern) pinnacle twice, and did a deep dive in the trough between the two main peaks to 210 feet. The visibility was terrific, and as we looked up toward the surface the light was dimmed by the numbers of snappers and almaco jacks that escorted us. Two huge manta rays swept by on one occasion — at 210 feet! Most times, we saw them only near the surface.

To use up our surface intervals profitably, Andy suggested we do some snorkeling while drifting across the top of the reef. Chito, our captain, would drop us 500 yards up-current (south) of the pinnacles, and the three of us would spread out and film what came by as we were carried along. For once the water at the surface was blue. We drifted through schools and schools of bonito mixed with Pacific crevalle and horse-eye jacks. The bonito were courting and mating, with groups of males chasing a female through the throng of bodies. The closest male would touch the vent or tail end of the female with his nose, which sent the female racing off, flashing and rolling, spraying a stream of eggs. It happened continuously as we watched; I expected at any second to see a 500-pound black marlin burst on the scene and take out a couple of bonitos. The suspense was permanent.

Below: Father coaches son on a sailfish.

Above: One of Jessica's friends, Sarah, in the garden of Tropic Star Lodge.

Because of its outstanding fishing and breathtaking setting, Tropic Star Lodge makes for a great family fishing vacation. For my children, Jessica and Alex, it's almost a home away from home. They have been many times, I think more for the parrots than the fishing. Still, Jessica has managed to catch nine of her 14 junior-angler world records at Piñas Bay, including a 79-pound almaco jack she caught on the reef and a 42-pound broomtail grouper off Punta Cariacoles. Alexander buttoned up a 108-pound sailfish at the same time Jessica was reeling in a 75-pound sailfish — a doubleheader of junior records.

The most memorable catch, though, was probably Jessica's first marlin, a fish she caught at the age of 5 with Stewart Campbell's help. Over the previous Christmas, I had been painting the big canvas of *Black Beauty*, which now hangs in the dining room at Tropic Star Lodge. Jessica liked to assist by filling in some bubbles, foam and water, and told me how much she wanted to catch a marlin. We went the following week to Tropic Star Lodge with Stewart, and on the second day a nice blue marlin ate the left rigger lure — a pink-and-white Softhead — and began its wild dance across the surface immediately behind the boat.

Jessica made straight for the chair. "Daddy, Daddy, that's my marlin — please give me the rod!" With the fish going ballistic, she insisted again, so when the marlin had calmed down somewhat, we got her in the chair. Stewart held the rod for her while she dropped the Shimano two-speed into a lower gear and fought the marlin for about 55 minutes. Capt. Isauro was at the helm, doing some exotic maneuvers, so we eventually caught up with the fish. When the mate, Olivio, grabbed the leader, the marlin treated us to a series of tail-walking leaps at the boat and then crashed broadside into the side of the boat. Jessica was thrilled as we tagged and released the 400-pound blue marlin. She finished off the day by catching and releasing four sailfish.

Of course, Alex has plenty of special moments on the reef as well. In January 2000, he caught his first grand slam, among the first reported in the new century. The day began with a small 200-pound blue marlin, which got tail-wrapped and unfortunately came up dead on arrival. It had been hooked before — a longline hook was in its jaw with a short length of cable leader festooned with goose barnacles. The next fish up was a sailfish, which Alex caught in quick time. As we now needed a black marlin to

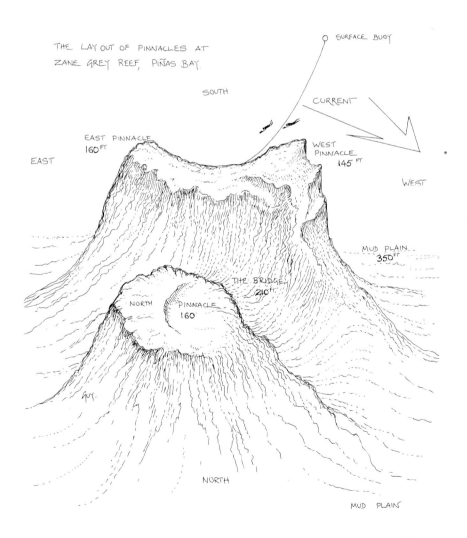

THE LAY OUT OF PINNACLES AT
ZANE GREY REEF, PIÑAS BAY.

SURFACE BUOY

SOUTH

CURRENT

EAST PINNACLE
160 FT

WEST
PINNACLE
145 FT

EAST

WEST

MUD PLAIN
350 FT

THE BRIDGE
210 FT

NORTH

PINNACLE
160

GUY

NORTH

MUD PLAIN

Above: Black Beauty, *acrylic on canvas.
This 12-foot-long painting hangs in the
restaurant at Tropic Star and remains one
of Harvey's favorite pieces.*

*Left: A sketch of the pinnacles that compose
Zane Grey Reef.*

complete the angling triple, Capt. Isauro headed back inshore to the reef, where we caught and put out three live bonitos.

Alex didn't have long to wait for his black — one ate the bonito on the left rigger, and the fight was on. The marlin jumped a lot but far away, and it was raining — not an ideal scenario for taking pictures. Alex fought the fish bravely for 65 minutes before he received assistance and then passed the rod over to our friend Charlie Murray. We could see the fish had a wrap of leader around its belly, so Alex had been fighting it the hard way. Charlie put the heat on the marlin and pumped it up in 10 minutes. On the wire, the fish did what all blacks do — it stayed airborne, enabling me to capture some of the action on film before tagging and releasing the 450-pounder.

As Jessica and Alex grew up, I let them do most of the fishing. Every time before we set off on a trip, I would spend an hour in the evenings for a week coaching them on correct angling techniques and procedures. This included removing the rod from the rod holder, fighting and pumping big fish, using the drag correctly and switching gears when necessary — all unassisted. Their ability, endurance and confidence increased, as did their enjoyment of the sport. Out at sea if things are slow, we look for signs of activity, such as birds, logs, dolphins and flying fish, and we discuss aspects of oceanography and the natural history of the fish they are trying to catch. In this way their knowledge and respect for marine life is continuously strengthened.

EXPLORING COIBA

Piñas Bay isn't Panama's only fishing wonder. The waters and banks surrounding the Coiba region are steeped in history, and the area's fishing and diving rank among the world's best. A number of islands and pinnacles surround Coiba, and all are great for diving, trolling and bottomfishing, particularly Isla Montuosa. Nearby Hannibal Bank is known for its outstanding big-game fishing.

The problem has always been gaining access to the region. Bob Griffin's famous Club Pacifico was closed down during the Noriega regime, and the succeeding government turned the area into a national park. Coiba remains a penal colony, so it is off-limits to the casual visitor, although sailing vessels and small cruise ships stop by the Coiba National Park daily.

In recent times, anglers have been able to sample this area's fishing aboard the *Coiba Explorer I* and *II* mothership operations. Owned by Mike Sanderson and Charlie Greer, *Coiba Explorer* utilizes a barge and eight 28-foot game boats to host both divers and fishermen. However, *Coiba Explorer* ceased operations as this book was being prepared.

The water around Coiba is generally clear, and d uring my visits there I have filmed a 500-pound black marlin off Montuosa, as well as blue marlin and lots of sailfish. Hannibal Bank has some monster sailfish in January and February, but the main attraction remains the drum-size yellowfin tuna most often found amid the schools of spotted dolphin between Jicaron, Hannibal Bank and Montuosa. On any given day, we could expect to find a school or two and target the yellowfin, some of which are very large indeed.

In late February 2001, I took Jessica and Alexander on a trip aboard the *Coiba Explorer* with the specific goal of catching tuna world records. We set out with the competent "Capt. Kid" at the helm, and the delightful, ever grinning "Chi-Chi" as mate. Using a 6-pound bonito as bait dragged just in front of a big porpoise school, Jessica managed a 198-pound yellowfin tuna in 40 minutes on 80-pound-test late in the afternoon of February 28, 2001, on the western side of Hannibal Bank. The following day, Alexander found a courageous 145-pound yellowfin off Montuosa that took him nearly an hour to land. I will never forget the look on his face when he lost 300 yards of line in just a few seconds after the bite. It must have been a daunting prospect to an 8-year-old to wind all that line back on the reel.

During the week, we dived with a myriad of jacks, triggerfish, rainbow runners and mullet snappers inshore, and snorkeled on drifting logs offshore. At Montuosa, Jessica fed the resident bull sea lion she named Oscar. In addition, they each caught four more junior angler records (snapper, almaco jack, roosterfish and a rainbow runner), bringing Jessica's record count to 14 and Alexander's to five.

Left: Harvey and Charlie Greer aboard the Coiba Explorer.

Below: Jessica landed this 198-pound yellowfin tuna off the Hannibal Bank to set an IGFA junior angler world record.

Opposite: Early Bite, *watercolor. Hannibal Bank is loaded with schools of spotted dolphin and big yellowfin tuna, escorted by opportunistic frigate birds.*

*A sailfish charges a triggerfish, separated from its
school under a floating log, in the acrylic and
watercolor* Oasis in the Blue.

*Right: The author videos a teased-up sailfish.
Despite its active pursuit of the bait, it remains
completely black.*

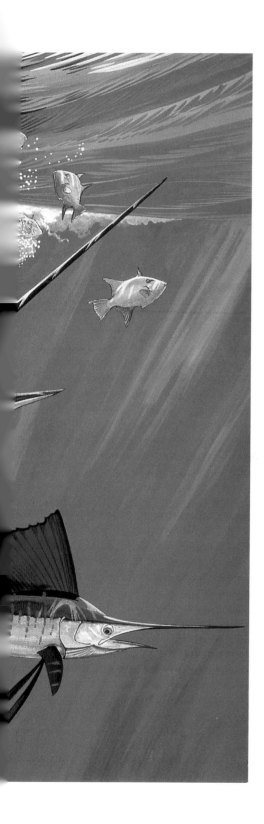

CHAPTER 15

GUATEMALA
Sailfish Mecca

When you want to perfect your angling techniques, whether using spinning gear, conventional gear or fly-fishing tackle, you want to go where you get lots of bites, a place with so many opportunities that it doesn't matter if you miss one fish or 20. The same applies to me when I'm filming them underwater. That is why, when embarking on my documentary about sailfish, I chose Tim Choate's world-famous Fins 'n Feathers Inn on the Pacific coast of Guatemala.

Thanks to the area's high catch rates since opening shop in 1994, Tim's operation has received a lot of ink from sport-fishing journalists worldwide. And it has been well justified. In 2000, for instance, the boats fishing out of Iztapa caught and released 10,076 billfish. The inn itself is one of the best-appointed fishing lodges I have been to. It has excellent food and accommodations, and a delightful couple, Louis and Patti Alicea, manage it. Anglers fish aboard six modern American sport-fishing boats, each with a captain and two mates. The crews — Capt. Bud Gramer on *Intensity*, Capt. Aron Valdez on *Magic*, Capt. Eric Lorentzen on *Classic*, Capt. David Salazar on *Yellowfin*, Capt. Brad Phillips on *Pelagian*, and the godfather, Capt. Ron Hamlin on *Captain Hook* — are world-renowned. Hamlin, in fact, pioneered the use of circle hooks for catching billfish, particularly sailfish. Today, you will not find a J-hook on any of the Fins 'n Feathers billfish rigs.

My first of several trips to film sailfish in Guatemala began in June 1998. I was joined by Jeff Ware and Leo and Anita Hooper on board Capt. Valdez's *Magic*, a boat I had fished previously when Tim had her based in Flamingo Bay, Costa Rica. Fishing at the same time on the *Intensity* was my compadre Kent Ullberg and his son Robert. The day we arrived Tim and his son Timothy went 25 for 45 on sailfish, so we knew a bite was starting. We loaded up the dive gear and cameras on the 31-foot Gamefisherman and headed out to "the spot," only 11 miles from the inlet. The plan was to pull four hookless lures as teasers and then switch over to baits when a fish was raised. I would

Sailfish seem comfortable with swimmers in the water, often passing close by the divers to reveal great color and anatomic detail.

The author paints in his Cayman Island studio, December 2000.

Right: Harvey painted the watercolor Sailfish on the Fly *after catching his first fish that way with Tim Choate aboard the* Intensity.

jump in as the boat slowed to a halt — the usual procedure. The teasers had been in for only 10 seconds when we raised a doubleheader of sailfish. I went over the side having barely had time to don my mask and fins.

One of the two fish proved very cooperative, staying with us for 20 minutes. The sail allowed me to carefully observe its repeated attempts to chew on the whole ballyhoo baits that were reinforced with floss stitching to hold the flesh together. The harder the mate pulled the line to get the bait away from the sail, the more it chomped on its catch, possibly thinking that the bait was escaping. If the mate allowed even a small amount of slack line, the sailfish would swallow the bait in a second.

We raised 12 sailfish in the first hour and 10 in the second. The other boats were seeing a lot of fish as well.

My best video came from sailfish that ignored me on the first charge. They would aggressively follow the Soft Head lures and swim right by me or over my head by a couple of feet. Some of the shy fish jammed on the brakes when they saw me and turned to one side, sometimes fading off and denying me the shot. In complete contrast, a hungry sailfish would attack the lures so aggressively that it put a wrap of the leader around its bill. Feeling the tension, it stopped and shook its head vigorously, freeing itself of the leader, but promptly turned around and attacked the lure repeatedly before transferring to the bait.

Having swallowed the bait, only to have the mate pull it out of its gullet, the sailfish would spin around and grab it again, stopping to crush and then swallow. It was amazing how some sailfish did not spook at getting wrapped in the leader and feeling the tension.

In addition to feeding behavior, color changes signaled different levels of excitement in the sailfish. Most feeding sails were simply jet-black — dorsal fins, backs, flanks and

even bellies. A really excited sailfish, perhaps one in six, has a bright, fluorescent-blue tail, while the rest of the body remains black.

After the excited sails hit a teaser or bait several times, they lost some of the sharp blackness, turning more bronze and green, with a bright-purple patch on the anterior part of the dorsal fins. The bronze band on their flanks ended abruptly at the white bellies, and pale, spotted stripes appeared down their bodies. If the sailfish turned and caught the sunlight, their backs and flanks would shine a burnished metallic green/blue and bronze; direct sunlight would change the color combination. When sailfish jump in air, their color is completely different from that underwater.

It remains a mystery why they appear so black when feeding. Some blue marlin assume that same black cloak, as we discovered in the Cape Verde Islands. What possible advantage could there be to appearing jet-black? Sailfish are schooling fish and cooperative feeders. It is logical to assume that with dorsal fins raised, big pelvic fins lowered and a black coloration, a sailfish appears much larger than it really is. With a group of sailfish surrounding a bait ball, escape may seem impossible for the corralled baitfish.

The sailfish quickly reverted to "cruising colors" when they became disinterested in the baits. I filmed several fish that in a matter of seconds went from jet-black to pastel blues and greens before swimming off, their dorsal fins down, pelvics and anal fins folded in the grooves along their bellies. In accelerating, they pulled all their fins in sharply, fitting into grooves or recesses in the skin for streamlining. I have seen this with all billfish species. Their bodies become pointed missiles driven by huge thrusters as they rapidly close in on their prey. As they approach, they slam on the brakes, and their fins open in a dramatic display. Waves of purple/blue iridescence wash through their dorsal fins, particularly if the crew uses a live jack or rainbow runner as the teaser bait.

Guatemala's sailfish were prolific. We jumped in on schools of up to eight fish, and I shot three rolls of film and a couple of hours of video that first day. We did not see any bait near the surface, but the captains were marking bait deep — 200 feet down — on their fathometers in water 400 feet deep.

That evening we watched all the footage on a big-screen television in the bar at Fins 'n Feathers. Leo and Jeff had taken turns with the second video camera and had done a great job; they were thoroughly enjoying their adventure. They had also caught 12 sails on circle hooks during the break we took from filming.

The following day was calm again, and we jumped in on 45 more sailfish. We had acquired more live bait from around a sea buoy on the way out, including a couple of 2-pound rainbow runners. I wanted to see what a sailfish would do with a big live bait. The next sailfish responded perfectly, but in its twists and turns to catch the rainbow runner, its bill caught and broke the thin 20-pound leader. The rainbow runner ran downward. The sailfish sounded, with me in hot pursuit, and caught the rainbow runner 100 feet down, almost out of sight. It crushed and swallowed the bait before heading back up into the spread, looking for more.

Although the next day proved windy because of a low-pressure system passing the coast, we dived on more than 30 sailfish, using live bait as teasers. We caught several sails to film the release sequence. I could swim right up beside the faces of these fish so the camera could catch clearly how the small circle hook had caught in the corner of the jaw. The configuration of the point and bight of the hook allow it to catch easily in the corner of the mouth, in contrast to a J-hook, which has a much wider bight and can lodge inside the stomach, throat or gills.

Most of the time, the circle hook will catch the corner of the jaw, which allows the fish to remain acrobatic without bleeding or ejecting its stomach. That leads to many more photo opportunities. At boat-side, the mate can put more pressure on the fish

Sunlight Sail — a "lucky" shot of a Pacific sailfish
going directly overhead.

A teased-up sailfish races past, presenting the perfect shot.

Right: A pair of sails chase the teasers. In Guatemala, the sailfish proved so prolific that fish often swam all around the boat and camera.

without fear of tearing any internal organs. For these and other reasons, circle hooks are best for these fish. Serious anglers and fishing-lodge owners should use nothing else when using baits for billfish.

In addition to pioneering the use of circle hooks for billfish, Guatemala crews have been at the forefront of catching sailfish on fly. In 2000, Fins 'n Feathers boats caught 875 sailfish on fly, and the *Magic's* Capt. Valdez holds the world record of 23 Pacific sailfish caught in a day on fly gear. Many anglers have caught their first billfish on fly here. I caught mine during this trip on the *Intensity* with Capt. Bud Gramer, and have become a convert. This is definitely the most exciting way to catch a sailfish. It involves the same teasing process we use for filming: Two crewmen tease the sailfish while the captain puts the boat in neutral and slows to a halt, creating flat, bubble-free water behind the transom. Even as a novice fly angler, I can cast the 20 feet of fly line required, and the fish usually responds immediately. Sailfish stay airborne for most of the fight, trying to dislodge the hook, and typically it takes no longer to catch them than when using conventional 20-pound tackle.

After catching a couple of fish on fly under Tim's guidance, I went overboard to film the fly bite. Tim cast to a teased fish, and the camera rolled as the sailfish ate the bright-pink fly just a few feet away. Once hooked, the sailfish did what I later found to be a common maneuver. It stopped swimming, nosed its head up in the water and shook its head furiously, bill swinging from side to side in a wide arc — a move known in angling parlance as "windshield wiping." At this point, the fish was so intent on shaking free this annoying spine in its mouth that I could swim right up to it while avoiding the thrashing bill.

After five to 10 seconds of this, the sailfish accelerated away and began jumping. Not being able to swim at 20 knots, I returned to the *Intensity* while Tim caught the fish. I then jumped back into the water to film as the mates expertly handled the tired sailfish at the boat and removed the hooks before releasing it.

After four days of great action, we planned a return trip for December 1999. This time, I brought documentary producer Diana Udel, her partner, Mike Massa, and Dave Warner. Tim Choate also came along to give good advice. Conditions were different during this trip, however; and we had to run 40 miles offshore to the continental slope to find the fish.

Capt. Bud Gramer told us that on the previous day a group of orcas had been working a school of spinner dolphin. Later in the day, while trolling teasers for sailfish in the same area, three orcas came into his spread — the big bull on the short left and a female each on the long left and right teasers. Incredible! What bait would you pitch to an orca? We came across the spinner dolphin and filmed them for a while. Later, we found a group of false killer whales, *Pseudorca*, harassing them. They caught and dispatched one dolphin not far from us. The big flock of gulls and terns over the spot told the story: life and death in the ocean.

We had a busy day. Diana was enjoying jumping in and filming the sailfish, one of which proved quite cooperative. A small blue marlin came into the spread, and I filmed it briefly before it departed. Presently we found a floating tree, upright in the water column, with roots about 50 feet down.

Floating trees provide a refuge for small bait fish. Many inshore species spend their early lives in the plankton, drifting great distances. They seek shelter from the flotsam as they grow; then when it approaches the shore, they abandon the floating tree and assume a benthic existence. In addition to the many varieties of reef fish, vast numbers of juvenile and adult pelagic species swam under the trees. These included green jacks, rainbow runners, rainbow chubs, mackerel scad, bonitos, bull dolphin and small yellowfin tuna down deep.

Harvey celebrates his first sailfish on fly with Tim Choate. Shortly afterward, the author went overboard to film the fly bite and release.

Tim Choate (center) with Maria and Alberto Iriarte, friends from Spain who joined in on a recent Guatemala expedition.

The author waits, ready to jump in on a raised billfish. In Guatemala, the wait usually wasn't a long one.

The bull dorado proved peculiar. When a diver approached, the front half of their bodies would turn a dark brown, and they swam in a humpbacked fashion, exaggerating the oscillation of their bodies. One fish that was hemmed in by two divers and a log stopped swimming briefly, wiggled its pectoral fins, opened its mouth and then closed its jaws, making a loud popping sound. It appeared to be submissive behavior, but I wondered at the purpose of it. A large predator of a dorado — a billfish or mako shark — would be quick to take advantage of such behavior and swoop in for the kill. Was the dorado trying to mimic the log and therefore avoid detection? Was the diver viewed as a threatening male and being told to keep clear? Nearby females did not exhibit these color changes.

Under some logs, I went to 80 or 100 feet down to shoot the log in silhouette with the baitfish around it. Down deep, I saw schools of yellowfin tuna, green jacks and skipjack. Whenever Capt. Gramer maneuvered the *Intensity*, the commotion and foam the boat made caused the yellowfin tuna to race upward to the surface to see what was going on. Foam is associated with feeding, and as I discovered in the Azores and Canaries, tuna respond without hesitation.

On a subsequent trip in November 2000, José Luis Beistegui and Alberto and Maria Iriarte from Spain accompanied me. We put them in the water on many sailfish and dorado underneath logs. Tim came with us again and coached Maria to her first sailfish on fly, with Capt. Brad Phillips on the *Pelagian*.

As a result of Fins 'n Feathers' success, other small marinas along the canal are opening and offering fishing trips in Guatemala's prolific waters. In 2000, Gary and Sheryl Carter from Atlanta, Georgia, fishing on their own boat, the 35-foot Cabo *Silverado*, caught and released 1,799 billfish for the year, with Gary catching 1,017 himself — a new unofficial record.

It is catch statistics like these that keep anglers returning time after time, which is why the inn is always booked out far in advance. Congratulations, Tim, Louis and Patti on the job you have done, as well as all the captains and crews who have enabled us to interact with the Pacific sailfish so frequently and successfully. No two fish are the same, and I am constantly learning something new about the ocean.

Blue Marlin on Small Yellowfin, *watercolor.*

*Dorado hang near a floating log. Note the defensive
color the males in the group display.*

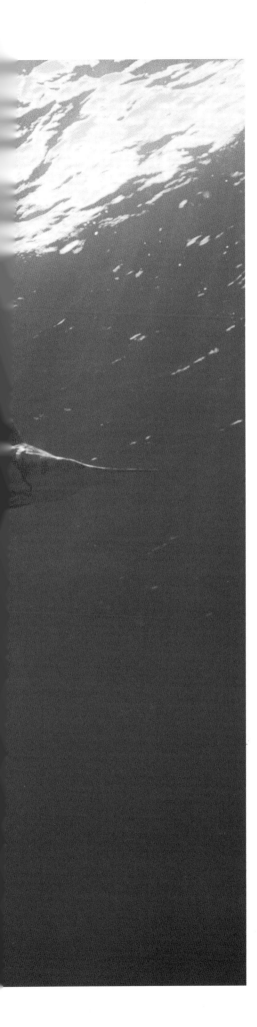

CHAPTER 16

Left: Harvey films striped marlin as they circle a bait ball.

Below: The motley crew — Harvey, Gary Graham, Bill Boyce, Charlie Forman, Kent Ullberg and Ray Barker Smith.

MAGDALENA BAY
A Magical Striped Marlin Encounter

O n most of my trips where filming free-swimming marlin ranks as the top priority, the call to attention usually comes with a simple shout from the bridge: "There he is on the long right!" When fishing the Thetis Bank off Magdalena Bay on the Pacific coast of Baja, Mexico, life isn't quite so orderly. More marlin than I could count working sardine bait balls in all directions produced a constant state of confusion that actually made filming difficult. But that's the kind of challenge I would welcome again in a heartbeat.

All I knew previously of Magdalena Bay came from random conversations and a couple of homemade videos. I had long heard stories of striped marlin by the hundreds from California skippers who fished the area as they moved north from Cabo San Lucas to San Diego. But any doubts I had about the accuracy of those stories vanished as I watched a video Dick Weber shot during a month of fishing the area in October 1999. Packy Offield's video of satellite-tagging striped marlin here was also staggering. So far as I knew, though, nobody had dived with the marlin on sardine bait balls, so I e-mailed Andy Byatt of the BBC and encouraged him to charter his own rig and spend time with us at Magdalena Bay in November 2000. He came through, along with famous underwater photographer Rick Rosenthal, to shoot footage for the *Blue Planet* series.

Joining me were Kent Ullberg, Bill Boyce, Charlie Forman and Mag Bay fly-fishing guru Gary Graham, of the Baja on the Fly fishing charter service. I had chartered Gary because he is an expert fly-fisherman, and the techniques of teasing billfish in for a fly presentation roughly mimic those required for filming them underwater. Our home for the trip was to be the 48-foot live-aboard *Garota*. With our group, three crew members, Gary's friend and guide from England, Ray Barker Smith, plus all our clobber, we figured to get to know each other quite well in the next few days.

After an interesting four-hour drive north from La Paz, we got to the dusty industrial fishing port of San Carlos. This town remains the only place between San Diego and Cabo San Lucas, at the tip of the Baja Peninsula, where a traveling boat can get fuel and supplies. The area is also known for its wonderful whale-watching, tardy customs officials and fine seafood. As usual, Bill was raring to go. "Let's grab a couple of cases of Dos Equis and vamanos!" Well, it took us two hours to dig up one case of cold beer in that little dust bowl.

In contrast to the arid land, the 150-mile-long Magdalena lagoon was bubbling with life. Pacific mackerel cram the waters here, so seabirds of all descriptions — pelicans, cormorants, frigates, boobies, gulls and terns — clog the masts and rigging of vessels as they move through the water.

It was blowing 18 to 20 knots as we meandered our way out of the lagoon and up to Thetis Bank on our first day. We pulled teasers, hoping for a striped marlin, but Gary warned us we were wasting time. "It's best to wait until we get to the zone," he said. He was right.

"The zone" is an easily recognizable area of predator/prey interaction, marked clearly by clouds of frigate birds. Although the water appeared off-color and was a cool 70 degrees, the place was full of fish life. In no time, we had a gang of marlin in the teasers. Blue tails, blue pectoral fins, blue stripes and rolling eyes were everywhere — where do you look?

That shouldn't suggest the plentiful fish made for easy filming. In fact, the plentiful bait balls were moving at tremendous speed and were difficult to keep up with, and the marlin proved impossible to keep on the teasers for long. We would repeatedly jump in ahead of the birds and bait balls, hoping they would swim to us, but we got only fleeting views of a cavalcade of bait, sea lions and marlin racing past.

In addition, the numerous Sei whales were working the bait schools hard. We would saunter up to a school and be just ready to go in when a Sei whale would come in and take the whole school in one gulp!

The action was so fast, and the situation so difficult, that Bill, Kent and I went into the water 40 times that day. By the time we were running in, we estimated we had filmed a hundred fish — not a bad start. We also caught one stripey on fly, which provided some release footage. We anchored up in Bahia Santa Maria, 8 miles from San Carlos, and had a delicious Mexican meal courtesy of Antonio, our chef. After dinner, we arranged to buy lobsters for the next day and filled the livewell with mackerel.

The second day proved very rewarding, even though the water was still green and rough. Nine other boats were fishing the bank, and most helped us keep tabs on the bait schools. Capt. Steve Lassley on *Mirage*, in particular, was a tremendous help throughout the week, pinpointing areas of activity. He directed us to a large school to the north of Thetis Bank, and we headed up there at full speed — 10 knots.

Once we arrived, Bill and I dived with some massive schools of small sardines that were feeding on zooplankton near the surface. Solid curtains of baitfish dimpled the surface in a "breezer," but surprisingly we saw no predators. We raised dorado and a few striped marlin a few hundred yards away, but it was as if the predators were waiting for reinforcements — or perhaps they were full.

We continued to troll teasers, raise fish and jump in. We got lucky on one cooperative striped marlin that stayed with us for 20 minutes. The crew did a magnificent job of teasing the fish with live bait and strips. This marlin came as close as any billfish I had dived with so far, and actually seemed to enjoy the game.

Later in the afternoon, the school of sardines rose to the surface and began feasting on the plankton again. The sky became choked with frigate birds, and I dived repeatedly trying to get a split shot with birds above the waterline and bait below. We finished off

The Magic of Magdalena, *watercolor.*
Frigate birds and brown and masked boobies
by the dozen circle over the bait balls driven to
the surface by striped marlin and sea lions.

*Above: A striper erupts on a bait ball from
below as Harvey gets the action on film and
Bill Boyce takes shots in the background.
Photo by Kent Ullberg.*

*Opposite: Harvey on a striped marlin.
Photo by Bill Boyce.*

the day by trying to catch a striped marlin on fly tackle, but our dedicated angler, Charlie, came up 0-for-8 in half an hour.

Conditions improved on the third day as winds died and water cleared. I started by filming a school of dorado around a shark buoy, and then filmed the release of a striped marlin we caught trolling for tuna. As the day progressed, we could see the flocks of frigate birds rising like smoke on a battlefield. They were everywhere.

Gary put us alongside a bait ball that had a group of striped marlin and sea lions around it. The school was zigzagging, but stayed pretty much in the same place. Three of us went in. I was so anxious, I lost a flipper. I turned to look for it, but the bait ball was in my face with a couple dozen striped marlin under my armpits, so I concentrated on the job at hand and forgot about the flipper.

This was it. This was the scene we wanted to stick with and film for as long as possible. A 300-sardine bait ball pulsed around and around, dodging this way and that, but not actually going anywhere. The three of us gathered on the sunny side of the school, about 15 feet below, and watched the show with cameras rolling, recording the phenomenon.

Just as I had seen with schools of white marlin in Venezuela and the Azores, and with schools of sailfish in Guatemala, only one fish attacked the bait ball at a time. The same individual may take several shots before pulling out, but is immediately replaced by the next marlin. This was no feeding frenzy, but an organized removal of prey by a conveyor belt of predators.

Too many marlin to count circled around, but well more than 20 remained at various distances away from the bait ball. They displayed normal swimming posture and color — the dorsal fin half up, anal fin tucked in and stripes muted. They circled and watched, circled and watched — until at some point it was their turn. The marlin would accelerate in toward the school, and suddenly the stripes would turn on, becoming so wide and vivid they appeared silver. The fish would extend all fins, but hold the pectorals in a low-slung position for increased maneuverability. The marlin would often make a false charge, shifting the bait school one way before turning in its own body length to attack in earnest with great acceleration and precision. It would catch one fish, stop swimming, crush the head and swallow it in a second before going back to the waiting station. If the marlin missed, it would repeat the process until it caught a sardine.

It was plainly obvious that the bill was not being used to slash at the school of bait. The marlin simply overtook the closest baitfish as it crashed through the school, picking off those not swift enough to escape. Baits that the raspy bill cut in two were collected quickly either by the initial marlin or another following close behind.

We had joined this bait ball quite late in the cycle. The marlin were accurate and successful; the bait had grown tired and slow to react. The marlin scored every time, and the stream of predators picked off sardines efficiently.

Paddling along with one flipper, I ran out of air in 30 minutes and continued to shoot from the surface while snorkeling. This introduced a whole new perspective. Luckily, it was calm at the surface, so I was able to hold the camera steady. However, I now became flotsam, and the sardine school took shelter under me, usually just in front of the camera. I tried swimming away to get out of the firing line and to present a more panoramic view of the action, but the bait school followed — as did the marlin — so I just hung there and continued to shoot.

The marlin continued to erode the school, but now they were taking sardines 3 and 4 feet away from the camera! They would come from under and beside me in a rush and take them; at no time did they brush against me. Some were so focused on the bait, they would come on to me *fast*, turning away at the last second just feet away, narrowly avoiding collision. It was nerve-racking, but it made for a good shot! It also

Bill Boyce focuses on a huge sailfish that
joined the action.

Above: The Magic of Magdalena II,
acrylic on canvas.

reinforced my observation that marlin avoid collisions at all costs, and perhaps helps explain why they take such an orderly approach to picking off a bait ball. Both these fish and the sailfish in Panama showed quite cooperative behavior; in fact, they even allowed sea lions their chance to feed.

On subsequent "experiments," we fed single live mackerel to a number of striped marlin around the boat. Two or three fish might sprint in after one fleeing mackerel, but always the trailing marlin cut the chase once a marlin was in position or had actually taken the mackerel. I've watched many other species of pelagic fish crash into each other and fight over bait hanging out of the predator's mouth. Tunas, jacks, tarpon, sharks and dorado all do this, but billfish apparently do not.

Having seen the huge shoals of sardines the previous two days, we surmised that the marlin go deep to break off a manageable group of sardines and drive them to the surface, where the birds above and the marlin below hem them in. We filmed eight different bait balls on our third day, each in different stages of

attrition. Some had been recently corralled. The marlin spent a lot of time circling, with the occasional false charge to keep the bait moving and thus tire the sardines. The fastest action came in the last few minutes of a bait ball's life when it had been consumed to fewer than 50 individual fish, with marlin scoring on every pass. All of a sudden, the bait would abandon the schooling instinct and split up in all directions, in threes and fours. Then the frenzy really began. All the marlin in the vicinity (often 50 or more) would kick into high gear and sprint after the fleeing sardines, engulfing them amid much foam and drama. And just as quickly as it began, it was over, and the marlin would wander off into the blue to look for another sardine bait ball.

Over the next few days, we witnessed the cycle of bait ball acquisition and consumption countless times. Yet at each encounter, there was always something new to observe. On one ball, a large sailfish joined the fray. This sailfish was over the 150-pound mark and dwarfed some of the striped marlin. In contrast to the brightly colored stripers, the sail remained completely black, just as I had seen in most other locations. It joined the group of circling marlin, following the exact same feeding process.

Harvey shoots a teased-up striper.
Photo by Kent Ullberg.

Most bait balls had sea lions and marlin mixed together. One sea lioness was particularly cooperative and allowed me to approach closely while she waited her turn at the bait ball. As she waited, she assumed a head-down position with her tail flippers up in the air. She kept a close watch on what was happening. When an opportunity arose, she quickly swam below the bait ball and attacked from underneath, catching a sardine in the middle of a perfect backward roll.

One constant was that the boat always proved a distraction to the marlin's feeding behavior. As we approached a bait ball and stopped, the sardines would seek shelter in the boat's shadow. I was concerned that the marlin would not attack the bait ball in this situation, but Gary assured me they would eventually drive the ball from under the boat and resume feeding. This was usually the case, but the marlin did lose the bait ball on one occasion.

One school of about 500 sardines was hanging in the boat's shadow when it suddenly dived vertically at full speed. It took the waiting marlin a couple of seconds to realize what was happening, but then about eight fish took to the chase at full speed, blue tails flashing with each stroke as they went out of sight below us. They quickly overtook the bait ball and forced it back up. We watched the bait reappear out of the deep blue in an unhurried and controlled manner, ringed by marlin. Close to the surface, the feeding began again.

On another dive, Bill and I watched the last of a bait ball expire and found ourselves in the water with lots of marlin hanging around, but no food for them to eat. I called out to Kent and Charlie on the boat to start throwing live mackerel in front of us, in hopes we could photograph some controlled shots of marlin feeding. The results were instant. The first couple of mackerel zoomed around at high speed, which allowed me to witness the marlin's agility. No matter how the mackerel turned, the pursuing marlin followed its every move and quickly overtook, grabbed, crushed and swallowed it. If one or two other marlin were in close pursuit, they would turn away once a front-runner had been established.

I wanted more control over the situation, so Kent clipped the tips of the mackerel's tails to reduce their swimming speed. The action now took place just a couple of feet in front of the camera. Underwater, the rush of the predator, the sound of it hitting the prey and the "pop" of the swim bladder were quite audible as the marlin crushed the mackerel.

Another marlin that was missing its left pectoral fin gave us a lesson in hydrodynamics. The fish was quite persistent; she ate 13 mackerel in front of the camera. When the bait landed in front, or to her right, she would sprint in and make a sharp right turn to take the mackerel. When the bait was presented on her left side, she would sprint in, but was unable to make the left-hand turn fast enough and would always lose out to another marlin. Here, right in front of me, was a live demonstration of how dependent the marlins are on their pectoral fins not only for lift, but also for maneuverability.

Bill was able to take many magnificent still shots of this interaction, while I shot video until we ran out of bait. The pectorally challenged marlin was none the worse for her disability; she looked big and fat and had surely learned to cope with her limitations.

The weather continued to favor us, and we spent the last two days building up the inventory of remarkable footage. But I distinctly remember one point late in the week when we three "marlineers" were on a bait ball thick with marlin — perhaps 30 or more fish — and I just had to stop filming and take in the scene. Here I was with two of my closest friends surrounded on all sides by feeding marlin, enjoying a glimpse of activity few, if any, had ever observed. What a privilege! That epiphany was a very moving moment for me, and to date ranks as perhaps the single most exciting event of my professional career.

Above: Jeopardy, *mixed media.*

Opposite: Avalon Harbor, Catalina Island.

CHAPTER 17

THE WEST COAST
Catalina, Alaska and Hawaii

Every year since 1989, I have exhibited artwork at the Fred Hall Western Outdoors Show in Long Beach, California, the largest fishing and outdoors show on the West Coast. After my first visit, I immediately realized I needed to create work specifically for the West Coast market, so species such as kelp bass (a.k.a. calico bass), California yellowtail, white seabass, and white, mako and thresher sharks started to feature heavily in my paintings. I accomplished most of my research for these pieces on several trips to Catalina Island, a beautiful, privately owned island off the coast of Southern California.

Catalina holds the distinction of birthing the sport of big-game fishing as we know it, and nowhere will you find more of this sport's history than at the Avalon Tuna Club. This exclusive club holds some of fishing's most significant memorabilia and all sorts of tackle from the pioneering days when anglers caught swordfish, striped marlin and big tuna, using equipment that is now regarded as antique.

I was surprised at the number of swordfish that still remain off Catalina, thanks at least partly to the absence of longlining. Commercial fishing takes place here, but in the form of harpooning, a very selective method of fishing. The same technique was used in the Northeast fishery before longlining all but removed the resource. My best chance of photographing a free-swimming swordfish may very well come in the waters off Catalina.

The water around Catalina usually remains blue and clear, the rocky bottom festooned with kelp forests that are home to a multitude of fish. Combinations of calico bass, sheepshead, garibaldi and yellowtail allow for colorful composition. Playful sea lions are plentiful. Few species, though, reside closer to the heart of California anglers than the white seabass, once the region's most popular game fish before being severely depleted by commercial fishing in the 1950s.

The white seabass has made a remarkable comeback in Southern California, and particularly off Catalina, largely because of the marine fish hatchery program Milt Shedd and family initiated. Shedd is an avid angler and the founder of Sea World and its research arm, the Hubbs-Sea World Research Institute in San Diego.

Guy Harvey

Chairman of the fishing tackle manufacturing firm AFTCO, Shedd began thinking about using hatcheries to restock the oceans in the mid-1970s. He focused on the white seabass, a tasty fish that can grow to 90 pounds, as a candidate. Stocks of the popular game fish were severely depleted, having dwindled to an estimated 10 percent of their former abundance.

Shedd provided seed money for the Hubbs biologists to conduct research on white seabass culture in 1982. While that team — led by Don Kent, who still heads up the work at Hubbs — developed the techniques for propagation, anglers turned to politics and began building support for the next step, a hatchery program. Shedd and other anglers asked to be taxed to pay for it, and in 1984 California lawmakers complied by approving the Ocean Resources Enhancement and Hatchery Program with a fishing license stamp, then $1 and now $2.65. Now the white seabass hatchery program operates in Carlsbad, California, as a partnership between the Hubbs Institute, United Anglers of Southern California, charter-boat operators, the California Department of Fish and Game and the San Diego Gas and Electric Company.

The hatchery raises eggs supplied by its resident brood stock into three-month-old fingerlings, which are then allocated to one of 12 "grow-out" sites along the coast from Santa Barbara to San Diego. Bill Shedd, son of Milt and a co-founder of United Anglers, led local fishing clubs to sponsor the grow-out facilities. Through their combined efforts, volunteers give more than 20,000 hours of time to the project annually. The sport fishermen who have witnessed the declining resource now have an opportunity to put something back. Once the fingerlings reach about 10 inches, the fish are released into the wild.

The success of the white seabass replenishment project marks only the beginning of the story, as researchers at Hubbs have already spawned other depleted species, such as halibut, black seabass, spotfin croaker and corvina. An integral part of the replenishment process is the banning of destructive, nonselective commercial fishing methods, such as the use of gill nets, and the enforcement of minimum sizes and daily catch limits for the recreational user group. Perhaps this technology will someday be applied to pelagic predatory species, such as sharks, billfish and tunas, before they are fished to the brink of extinction.

O n one of my West Coast trips, I made an important stop in Jackson, Wyoming, where I attended the inauguration of America's first and only Wildlife Art Museum. Kent Ullberg introduced me to many famous wildlife artists from all over North America and even Europe. While the depth and quality of the paintings and sculpture there humbled me, I was amazed at the lack of marine wildlife art present, especially when I considered the thousands of miles of coastline that surrounds North America and that 70 percent of the planet is covered in seawater!

While in Wyoming, Kent and I took advantage of the great weather and visited Yellowstone National Park. We also fly-fished for cutthroat, rainbow and brown trout, absorbing the incredible scenery of Les Grands Titons while being paddled down the Snake River by our expert guide.

Farther north is the amazingly beautiful wilderness of Alaska. No picture does this place justice, I was told; you just have to see Alaska for yourself. My chance finally came in June 1997 when Ricky Smith and Jay Gustin invited my family and me to spend a few days aboard Jay's 60-foot Delta, the *Adventurous*, based in Sitka. They wanted me to catch and research the species of the region and turn my experiences into art.

We sailed south along the coast from Sitka, meandering through the fjords and

Above: Harvey, Kent Ullberg and Lars Jonssen pose with Kent's sculpture, Waiting for Sockeye, *at the American Wildlife Art Museum in Jackson Hole, Wyoming.*

Opposite: Calico Bass, watercolor.

islets taking in the grand, wild vista of mountains, sky and sea. Here and there a sea otter popped up, seals glided by and sea lions stretched out on the rocks taking in the warm sun. Gulls and bald eagles wheeled overhead. Our home for the next three days was Whale Bay, where we caught chinook (king) salmon by the score, interspersed with a few coho. Our mate, Travis Petersen, was superb in the cockpit. He showed us how to rig the herring bait and use the downriggers. Jessica and Alex quickly became accomplished at catching salmon on single-action reels, and that's where Jessica caught her first IGFA Junior Angler World Record, a chinook of 28 pounds, at the age of 7.

Whale Bay is appropriately named. Many humpback whales swam in the area, feeding on the abundant sand eels (needlefish) and herring. We would be stopped and fighting a fish, when whoosh! — a Humpback would blow just yards away from us. At the end of the day's fishing I made notes and did a lot of sketches of the whales, birds, kings and coho, as well as details of the fish they consumed. Gradually, the encounters spawned ideas for more elaborate paintings.

Each evening we anchored up in a different cove in one of the fjords of Greater or Lesser Whale Bay and had fresh salmon for dinner. Some evenings we set a group of small traps baited with a salmon head in deep water. The next morning they would be loaded with bright-red coon shrimp and spotted shrimp, which Jessica and Alex meticulously sorted into different species piles before they made their way to the menu.

One morning at low tide, Jay and Travis took us ashore up an unnamed river mouth. We walked up to a set of falls and fished in waders for coho and Dolly Varden using artificial lures. Jessica was lucky and caught several of each while I wandered around soaking up the scenery, watching the salmon scale the waterfall. Gradually the tide came in right up to the base of the falls, and the water below was jammed with salmon on their way up to their natal stream. This was a far cry from my blue-water sojourns, searching for a blue marlin in the waters so much farther to the south or, as I would discover a year later, to the west.

I made my first journey to the Big Island of Hawaii in 1988 to present a paper at the Second International Billfish Symposium. Hawaii is one of the world's great big-game fishing destinations, and for me to actually participate in the conference was a double dream come true, since the conference was held in conjunction with the annual Hawaiian International Billfish Tournament, one of the most prestigious fishing events in the Pacific.

I returned to Hawaii for several years to participate in the HIBT with the Laguna Niguel Billfish Club and fished with angling greats Brooks Morris, Bob McIntosh, Jim Luden and Gil Kramer. Their team won the HIBT in both 1985 and 1986 when Gil caught a Pacific blue marlin world record of 1,062 pounds on 50-pound tackle.

In 1992, I accompanied the terrible trio of Charlie Forman, Raleigh Werking and Kent Ullberg as the official IGFA team. Tournament organizer Peter Fithian had invited Kent and me to exhibit our artwork during the event. The show was a great success, and the first of several we did together in Kona. I also attended IGFA and Pacific Ocean Research Foundation meetings on my visits there.

Our efforts in the fishing arena weren't quite so productive, though.

In 1994, I entered the first Jamaican team, under the appropriate name of "Cool Runnins." Dressed in our outrageous costumes and dreadlocks, we came away with the trophy for best costume. But that's where our success ended; we scored only a single ahi (yellowfin tuna) in the main event. I had no idea reggae music

Below: Jessica Harvey and her first world record, a king salmon of 28 pounds caught in Whale Bay.

Above: The Adventurous *served as mothership for exploring Alaska's beautiful shorelines.*

Opposite: Yellowstone Cutthroat Trout, *watercolor.*

Guy Harvey

Yellowstone Cutthroat

Above: Humpback Family Off Big Island,
mixed media.

Opposite: Hawaiian Blue, *watercolor.*
A father-and-son team take on a blue marlin
in their outrigger canoe.

was so popular in Hawaii, but our team shirts featuring my *Reggae Marlin* design proved to be a collector's item. One such shirt sold for $400 in the HIBT auction, money that went toward billfish research in the Pacific.

One of my most enjoyable expeditions to Hawaii occurred in March 1995. I was on a mission to film free-swimming shortbill spearfish, and few places have as many around as Kona normally does in March and April. Raleigh Werking and I chartered the delightful couple Kelley and Jocelyn Everett on their beautiful Merritt *Northern Lights* for five days. But my run of poor luck with fishing in Kona continued. I didn't see a spearfish all week, though I did managed to catch and photograph a pretty little striped marlin of about 60 pounds.

Since that time the tournament catch results have become progressively poorer. The consistent depletion of billfish due to commercial longlining, and to some extent by the recreational angling sector, had contributed to the reduced international participation in Hawaiian billfish tournaments by the late 1990s, and has had a negative impact on the charter industry.

Of course, fishing has never served as my primary attraction to Hawaii. Actually, the islands themselves provide inspiration enough. One of the limitations I find in painting oceanic predators is the monotony of the blue background. Most pelagic fish are found far offshore, denying me the opportunity to realistically involve detailed environments, as can be done when painting birdlife or big-game animals.

Hawaii is a rare exception. Along with other oceanic islands, where deep nutrient-rich water comes close to shore, Hawaii gives me an opportunity to include majestic scenery with the fishing scene or behind the predator/prey interaction. Hawaii's high volcanic mountains, cliffs and old lava flows provide some of the most interesting and dramatic backdrops for game fish and whale paintings I've yet encountered.

The Hawaiians have fished for centuries using hand lines from outrigger canoes. This historical link with the sea conjures up epic struggles with giant blue marlin and big ahi, similar to those illustrated in the *Old Man* series. Added to this is the beauty of the Hawaiian people, their customs, culture and indigenous wildlife. It's no wonder that artists, authors and photographers have flocked to these islands for inspiration, just as I have.

CHAPTER 18

Left: A big black marlin looks huge with Charlie Forman in the background. This image is the author's favorite underwater billfish shot.

Below: A cooperative black of around 300 pounds.

AUSTRALIA
The Blacks of Great Barrier Reef

Whenever planning my earliest billfishing trips, I always cast an envious eye toward the continent of Australia. I knew Australia offered the ultimate heavy-tackle fishing experience for marlin, but the costs involved were considerable. During a fishing trip to Costa Rica with Aussie skipper Laurie Wright and his wife, Julie, however, I got an earful about the big black marlin of the Great Barrier Reef. That was the final bit of encouragement I needed, so in October of 1990 I teamed up with Raleigh Werking, the late Rus Hensley and his son Clay for 10 days of fishing.

Laurie had recommended we use a mothership operation to accommodate our diving and fishing interests, and to allow us to visit different areas of the Great Barrier Reef, following the marlin as they traveled north. So on our arrival, Laurie captained the game-fishing boat *Balek III*, a 40-foot Woodnutt, while John Stoddart and his wife, Linda, ran the mothership, a quaint Norman Wright-built, wooden-hulled vessel called *Bali Hai*.

Laurie had been a mate for his well-known namesake, Peter B. Wright, but had since been running his own charter operation for several years during the short Cairns giant black marlin season. For the rest of the year, he and Julie ran the *French Look*, a 46-foot Merritt in those days, for Jean Paul Richard. Our two deckies were Sean Wallace and Peter Duboise.

On that first trip, we each caught two blacks and lost twice that number. Rus was delighted to catch his first black, a 150-pound fish off Ruby Reef. Clay caught a 200-pound fish, and Raleigh a couple of 300-pounders. I got a 300-pound black and

*Barrier Reef Rendezvous, acrylic on canvas.
One of Harvey's largest paintings, the piece had
to be long enough to accommodate all the fish
and capture the scene.*

another around 800, which was the only large fish we caught that trip. Rus had a "nice fish" on for a zip, but we never got a look at the thousand-pounders that have made this reef famous.

The most memorable part of that trip was our encounter with a group of marlin late one afternoon. Raleigh had just caught, tagged and released a 300-pound black off No. 5 Ribbon Reef when Laurie called me to join him — quickly! — in the tower.

The sea was running high, with a 20-knot southeasterly wind working against the current. A hundred yards away to our right, seven male marlin escorted a female of immense proportions. The group of black marlin were swimming fast down-sea into the current, disappearing and reappearing, flashing their neon-blue bodies on and off. The males, all approximately 200 pounds, were jockeying for position, changing colors depending on how the evening sun lit up their iridescent bodies — metallic bronzes,

greens and brilliant blues and purples. It was a cavalcade of black marlin.

Laurie edged the *Balek III* closer to intercept them — and maybe get a bite. Only one male swung over and lazily looked at the scaly mackerel on the left rigger before joining the group again. I was more interested in watching the proceedings than catching a fish. We were able to track the group of marlin for another five minutes, and we watched the males swim up alongside the big female. It was quite likely she was spawning eggs in a constant stream, as the males took up position beside her to shed their milt before dropping back to allow another male to move in.

Even though I did not have a camera, I contemplated jumping in to have a quick look. That event occurred years before I began eagerly hopping overboard to dive with marlins, so I hesitated and stayed on board — a decision I have always regretted, as it was the only time I have seen such a spawning aggregation of marlin. I did, however, paint the scene from memory and named it *Barrier Reef Rendezvous*. Sean said he had once seen 22 marlin in a spawning group, including three big females.

October 27 was a good day. We raised six black marlin, had four bites and caught two. At 3:10 p.m., it was my turn. Two fish came up, a small one that ate the big bonito bait but dropped it, and a big female that sneaked in and ate the scad on the right rigger. I remember seeing the first jump, quite far away — the huge head, thick bill, small eye and spread pectoral fins, an image I had seen in so many photographs and videos, and now I had one on! Clay did a great job of taking photographs on my 35mm camera — I came terribly unprepared where photography was concerned — and when Peter Duboise wired the marlin for release, the boat-side action was spectacular.

We entered the "Halloween Tournament" that year and got a bite out of a noteworthy fish, an approximate 700-pounder that was clearly visible near the surface from 500 yards away. Laurie was in the tower as always and called me up to look. The whole fish lit up from stem to stern — a bright blue glow in the water. Laurie explained that there would be other male marlin nearby, escorting this big female. Sure enough, a couple of them came into the spread. She joined them and with great speed and determination took the lure on the right rigger, but the hook did not stick properly.

Every day was an adventure on the reef. We dived every morning after breakfast and before going to look for fresh bait around the reef heads ("bommies"), hand-feeding giant Queensland groupers (similar in size and shape to the jewfish) and potato cod off the back of the mothership. Laurie took us to some great spots: Temple of Doom, Pixie Bommie and the Cod Hole. We caught giant trevally, Spanish mackerel and dogtooth tuna behind the reef, and at night after dinner we bottomfished from the mothership. It was a great experience, and after my 10 days were up I stayed on for another six with Al Hooper, the owner of the *Balek III*, to spend more time diving and taking notes on species for my paintings. At the time, I was making a push with the Guy Harvey line of sportswear in the Australian market, so the time spent familiarizing myself with the fish and coral species proved invaluable. My journal is full of reference material.

My next visit to the Great Barrier Reef came in November 1993, but this time we were a group of eight. Joining me were friends Ray Miles, Roger Turner, Charlie Forman, his wife, Sue Ann, and Dr. Don Goodwin, along with my elder brother, Jonno, and brother-in-law, Jonathan Collier, both of whom live in Perth. It was a great reunion for the family members.

Armed with a new Nikonos state-of-the-art underwater camera, this time I was prepared for the expedition when we met with Laurie Wright and mates Troy and Rob in Cooktown. We didn't have to wait long for something to photograph.

On our first day of fishing, I released a black marlin of about 350 pounds, followed the next day by a small 150-pounder for Charlie and another for Ray — his first black — on our third day. An amazing thing happened with this fish. The fishing had been slow, so Troy put a scad on a downrigger, and presto — a bite, but no hookup. He reeled up the downrigger ball and left it a few inches below the surface, right behind the boat, while he went to let out another scad. The marlin ate the scad, and Ray *san cochoed* the fish, reeling in only a head.

Laurie put the *Balek III* into a tight right turn to come back on the fish and shouted down from the tower, "The fish is under the boat!"

Lit up blue from end to end, the marlin had the lead downrigger ball in its mouth and was veering away off to the left. The drag on the reel pulled the ball away, but the marlin grabbed it immediately and sounded, pulling drag on the

Below: Dr. Don Goodwin works hard on his first black marlin.

Above: Harvey with elder brother Jonno, who was a top prawn skipper along Australia's northern coast.

Opposite: Dogtooth Tuna and Fusiliers, watercolor.

heavy downrigger reel. Troy brought the weight back up, but before he could get it out of the water the marlin grabbed it for a third time, again pulling drag on the reel before letting go. Meanwhile Rob fired out another scad on Ray's rod, and the fish pounced on the bait. Ray made no mistake this time. The marlin jumped repeatedly close to the boat, and I was able to get some good shots before it was released. Afterward, I observed the downrigger ball as it hung a few inches below the surface behind the transom, leaving a beautiful bubble trail. It looked just like a big lure — no wonder the marlin had wanted it.

It was Don's turn next, but we entered a dry spell — not a day or two, but five days straight without a black marlin bite. We did everything we could to attract a fish in the slick-calm weather, and each day the pressure kept mounting on the indomitable Capt. Laurie. On the evening of the fifth day with no bites, Jonno, the comedian, presented him with a plain white T-shirt bearing the five "doughnut" Olympic rings painted on with a magic marker. Below were the words, "Congratulations, Captain Pentanaught." I thought Laurie was going to cry! Of course, it could have been worse. Peter Wright on the *Duyfken* was fishing next to us and went seven days without a bite. In fact, his charter that week did not get a single black marlin bite — a long way to travel for nothing, but that's fishing. The two things you cannot control are the weather and the fish, which explains why everything changed dramatically the following day.

Above: The awesome team of Laurie and Julie Wright.

In a break from tradition, we fished from dawn until 9:30 a.m., stopping only for breakfast and a dive before resuming our fishing. This particular day had been calm and ideal — just like the previous five — except that at 2 p.m. a fish appeared on the right rigger and ate the scad. Don fought the fish for 40 minutes, and it jumped only once. Even from that distance, we could see it was a monster. We had the fish less than 100 feet from the boat when the rod tip started to jerk violently. The sharks had found the marlin immediately below and were tearing into it. Although the carnage was taking place out of sight, it was a sickening feeling to have brought about the destruction of this great fish. All that was left was the tail that had gotten wrapped in the leader before the sharks had cut through the marlin's backbone and the #19 wire. That tail was 54 inches wide with a girth of 20 inches at the peduncle. We estimated her weight at 950 pounds.

At 3:05 p.m., a black marlin ate the scad on the right rigger and Jonno fought it for quite a while, getting "frogged" in the chair a couple of times — much to the amusement of Laurie, Troy and Rob, who had been on the receiving end of a lot of lip the past five days. Jonno caught his first black marlin of 400 pounds the hard way, foulhooked in the shoulder.

At 4 p.m., I was in the tower talking to Laurie and watching the baits. He was looking at something in the distance, when a huge black marlin crashed the skipping scaly mackerel on the left rigger. The fish came from underneath, going vertically into the sky and clearing the water by several feet, almost to the point that it was in line with me in the tower. It hung there for a moment, with the mackerel in its jaws, and then fell away from the boat making a huge splash. That scene remains burnt into my memory not only because of the fish's size, but also because of the great predator's explosive appearance.

I scrambled down the tower to get my camera and saw Jonathan fixed to the deck as if in a trance — rod still in the holder. The line was crackling off the spool, and the great fish, having eaten the scaly mackerel, was racing across the wake to eat the swimming scad on the right rigger — pulling 45 pounds of drag all the while. Jonathan, at 6 feet 6 inches and 280 pounds, can tackle most things, but in this case he passed the rod. He had been standing in the cockpit, dutifully watching the baits, when the black marlin rocketed into the air behind the boat. From his perspective as a relatively

Left: The Bali Hai *and* Balek III *anchor at Lizard Island.*

inexperienced angler, it must have seemed vast, intimidating and impossible to catch.

Turns out, it was impossible to catch. The marlin never jumped again, and I pulled the hook on it after 28 minutes. "Big Julie" was gone.

The baits were out again. By 5:15 another black marlin crashed the skipping bonito. Jonathan jumped into the chair and made short work of the 600-pound fish, powering her in for tagging in just eight minutes. There was a great mood on the *Bali Hai* that evening as we celebrated the demise of the "Doughnut Factory."

Having had a lot of success filming marlin and sailfish in 1994 and 1995 at Cocos Island, I was confident that on my next trip to Australia's Great Barrier Reef I could get some underwater photographs of free-swimming black marlin. I had not tried in Piñas Bay, Panama, because the water was usually quite green with poor visibility.

This time the team was reduced to four — me, Kent Ullberg, Charlie Forman and his wife, Sue Ann. We hooked up with Laurie and Julie again on the *Balek III* and the *Bali Hai* — none the worse for wear after the antics of our memorable trip two years earlier. Laurie's deckies were Troy Dallman and Kiwi John Batterton.

Loaded to the hilt with camera gear, we planned to tease in the black marlin on a lure or lure/bait combination, and I would go in to shoot stills on the Nikonos while Charlie shot video. Laurie approved the plan. He is the type of captain who will try anything, and teasing and filming sounded just as exciting as catching. His only concern was the reaction from the shark population; they are numerous, large and aggressive, and, as we had witnessed previously, could take a hooked marlin apart in minutes. We decided not to film any hooked fish, believing this would push the risk factor beyond an acceptable limit. We also chose to play it safe and put out hooked baits in the late evening and along certain parts of the reef — particularly in the passes — where Laurie considers it foolhardy to dive.

On November 11, off Agincourt Reef, we dived on the first black marlin we raised. It was near a school of feeding skipjack, just a half-mile off the drop. The marlin was all over a big Softhead/queenfish combination and very cooperative. I got a whole roll of film on this fish; the crew did a great job of teasing with strips and a whole bonito. The marlin almost ate the bonito, as I had hoped it would since I wanted to see how it would handle a big bait. Charlie shot several minutes of good video as silvertip sharks came out of the blue to check us out. "No worries, mate," they seemed to say, as they swam away and down after only one pass.

Below: "Why Me?" Don Goodwin waited five days to hook this big marlin, only to have the sharks take it.

Opposite: Balek III and Big Julie, *watercolor.*

The next day we moved farther north after diving between St. Crispins and Agincourt #1. We raised seven black marlin for the day, but they proved difficult to tease in. Charlie and I jumped in on a fish that was lit up and tracking well, but all we saw in the water were a couple of big whaler sharks. A lot of marlin were tailing in the waves and giving the teasers only a cursory glance. They were all small fish, less than 300 pounds.

On November 13, we dived on two marlin — a black of about 150 pounds in the late morning and a second fish of about 250 pounds with a bill curved downward in the extreme, giving it the appearance of an ibis or a curlew. This marlin's back was also very black and had silvery flanks. It turned a pastel blue when it faded off and swam away. We decided to use live bait on the next marlin to see if they would stay around longer. We caught some bonitos and rainbow runner and kept some of them in the livewell.

After an exhilarating dive at the Temple of Doom bommie the next morning, we ran north inside the reef and then started to fish at the north end of No. 6 Ribbon Reef. We raised a small marlin at 11 a.m., but we could not tease it in. Soon afterward, a bigger fish crashed the bonito on the left side. As quickly as Troy tried to get the bait away from it, it came on for another strike. I went in.

The marlin was on my side of the boat for a change, so I was going to have a good chance at a clean shot. The marlin grabbed the head of the bonito, and Troy pulled it away again. The fish turned and came streaking toward me; I fired off eight shots as the marlin swept by. In the background, Charlie had just jumped in. I was now waiting for the fish to spin around and eat the rainbow runner that was supposed to be there. The marlin swam up to the boat before heading off down-sea. I was disappointed to see such an active fish leave the scene so early in the teasing process. Where was the rainbow runner?

Above: A black marlin chases a teaser while below, out of the picture, silvertip sharks circle.

Opposite: Coral Trout, *watercolor.*

At that moment, I felt a line tangle in my regulator; it was the bait line. Where was the bait? I looked around and discovered it under my body, hiding from the hungry marlin. The marlin had charged in to take the live bait, which had then sought refuge under me as it swam by. Although I managed to get the shot, we discovered the importance of keeping the live bait away from the divers in the future.

After reaching No. 10 Ribbon Reef, we spent three consecutive mornings diving at the Cod Hole, feeding the giant potato cods, trevally, red bass and Maori wrasse. It proved a truly unique experience, rivaled only by feeding the rays at Stingray City in the Cayman Islands or the Caribbean reef sharks at Walker's Cay, Bahamas.

Feeding potato cod reaching 100 to 250 pounds is not for the faint of heart. Laurie kept his food in a plastic bag in a heavily weighted 5-gallon bucket so it stayed firmly on the bottom. Once we took up position on a sand patch, the cod would try to knock us over to get to the bucket. We had to retaliate to let them know who was in charge. Gloves and a long-sleeved wetsuit were mandatory,

Guy Harvey

since an arm can end up inside a cod's mouth in a blink. Once we got the hang of it, though, feeding them was exciting and a wonderful experience.

On November 16, on the way back from Cod Hole, Laurie spotted a small whale shark in Dynamite Pass. It swam in a docile manner and appeared to be gulping plankton at the surface. We spent half an hour in the water taking photographs of this amazing creature.

Once we left the whale shark, we decided to get some fishing in and put out the guns. We got more than we bargained for when Kent caught a 600-pound whaler shark on a live bait. The shark looked huge by the boat, and it was easy to see how a pack of these could make short work of a hooked marlin. Then the tiny fish moved in, and Kent went 1-for-4. The black marlin he caught may have weighed 70 pounds; it would have been great on 12- or 16-pound-test instead of 130-pound. We were fishing for thousand-pounders, however, which could show up at anytime.

As fishing became slower, we spent more time diving. Laurie took us on some drift dives on the incoming tide in the passes — wide gaps on the reef with deep water and fast current as water races in and out on the changing tides. Laurie used a surface buoy to mark our position from the *Balek III* because we would be moving as fast as 4 knots along the edge of the reef. This procedure proved a great opportunity to meet some of the large pelagics. As we were swept along, we raced through schools of barracuda, Spanish mackerel, big dogtooth tuna, trevally, rainbow runner and, of course, a number of reef sharks and some silvertips. After flying along for several hundred yards, we would break out of the current and swim behind the reef head to take a closer look at the Maori wrasse, coral trout and big Napoleon fish, a species that resembles a huge green parrotfish with a battering ram on its forehead.

Following this eventful expedition on the Great Barrier Reef, we stayed for a couple of days at Laurie and Julie's farm up in the Atherton Tableland. This is a most beautiful area of Queensland, with incredible birdlife supported by an exotic rain forest — a naturalist's paradise.

What a place to live! Reef on one side and forest-covered mountains on the other. I shall return.

Left: Harvey feeds a huge potato cod at the famous Cod Hole along No. 10 Ribbon Reef. Photo by Kent Ullberg.

Opposite: Countless species inhabit the extensive reef system, including (top to bottom) Maori wrasse, coral cod and red bullseye.

INDEX

EPILOGUE

I've had the pleasure of working on the *Marlin* magazine team since 1988, and I cannot recall a time during that tenure when Guy Harvey didn't reign as the pre-eminent artist in the sport-fishing world. Several other talented artists have carved out niches in this industry for themselves, but no one has taken sport fishing into the public eye like Guy has through his recognizable art and marketing prowess.

Over the years, I've had the pleasure of working with Guy on numerous occasions. He has provided artwork for *Marlin* often, and the magazine has commissioned him for original works to go on several covers, including those for our 10th and 20th anniversary issues.

Back in 1995, *Marlin* debuted the results of Guy's work with free-swimming billfish with an article titled "Close Encounters." Filled with excellent shots of striped marlin and sailfish taken off Cocos Island, that piece carried the cover blurb: "Guy Harvey Takes the Plunge with Free-Swimming Billfish." It was a prophesy we didn't appreciate at the time, for what a plunge it has turned out to be.

In editing this book, I came to appreciate more than ever that Guy Harvey is much more than a painter of fish. A biologist, photographer, adventurer, diver, philanthropist, conservationist, ambassador and angler, Guy has never been satisfied in simply illustrating the sport-fishing world. He has worked tirelessly to improve it. His art has helped enlighten people everywhere on the plight of pelagic species and marine mammals, and his underwater work with free-swimming fish is teaching anglers the world over about the feeding behavior of marlin, sailfish, spearfish, tuna, sharks and a host of other species.

Guy's success in this business has been hard earned and is well-deserved. I look forward to working with him in his continuing efforts to learn more about the marvelous inhabitants of our oceans and to teach others in the process.

David Ritchie
Editor